The Industrial Archaeology of Farming in England and Wales

The Industrial Archaeology of Farming in England and Wales

Nigel Harvey

B T Batsford Limited, London

First published 1980

© Nigel Harvey 1980

ISBN 0 7134 1845 1

Photoset by Photobooks (Bristol) Ltd,
28 Midland Road, St Philips, Bristol BS2 0JY

Printed by Redwood Burn Ltd,
Trowbridge and Esher
for the publishers B T Batsford Ltd,
4 Fitzhardinge Street, London W1H 0AH

To Barbara, with love

By the same author

The Farming Kingdom
Farm Work Study
The History of Farm Buildings in England and Wales

In the National Federation of Young Farmers Clubs series of booklets
The Story of Farm Buildings
Ditches, Dykes and Deep Drainage

In the Shire Publications series
Old Farm Buildings
Fields, Hedges and Ditches
Farms and Farming
Discovering Farm Livestock

As 'Hugh Willoughby'
Amid the Alien Corn (Published in the USA)

In press for Ministry of Agriculture, Fisheries and Food Reference Book series
Effective writing in advisory work (With Graham Cherry)

Contents

The Industrial Archaeologist & The Farmer

There is much to interest the industrial archaeologist in the farmlands. But visitors to the countryside are reminded that farms are the private workplaces and homes of farmers and should never be entered without the permission of the occupier.

List of Illustrations

Line drawings in the text

The bracketed numbers in the text indicate the references at the end of
the book (pages 180–223)

Acknowledgments

The Author and Publishers would like to thank the following for their permission to reproduce illustrations in this book: Aerofilms Ltd (2, 10, 17, 23, 24, 26, 27, 70, 72); Ashmolean Museum (9, 12, 16); The Warden and Fellows of All Souls College M.W. Beresford and J.K.S. St Joseph (line drawings, page 48); Cambridge Antiquarian Society (5); Committee for Aerial Photography, University of Cambridge (6 – copyright reserved); Farmers Weekly (3, 4, 8, 11, 21, 28, 29, 64, 65); John Gray (67); Geoffrey Hammond (30); J.A. Hellen (59, 60); J.L. Henson, Cotswold Farm Park (31); Hereford Times (62); Lackham College of Agriculture (61); Ministry of Defence, Air (15, 19, 22 – Crown copyright); Museum of English Rural Life, Reading (18, 25, 32, 33, 39, 40, 41, 42, 43, 44, 45, 47, 52, 66, 74); National Museum of Wales, Welsh Folk Museum (58, 68); J.E.C. Peters (73); Peter J. Reynolds, Butser Ancient Farm Project (7); Royal Commission on Historical Monuments (1); Science Museum (13, 34, 35, 36, 37, 38, 46, 48, 49, 50, 51, 53, 54, 55); Pamela Toler (20); Reece Winstone (63); C. Woolf (56).

Illustration 69 is based on C. Waistell, *Designs for Agricultural Buildings*, 1827, plates VII and VIII and No. 71 on T. Sturgess, 'Farm Buildings', *Journal of the Royal Agricultural Society of England*, 1850, pp. 288–300.

Acknowledgments for help received in collecting information are given in the appropriate reference.

Introduction

The farm begins with the plant, which is the only means known to man of converting inorganic compounds which he cannot eat into organic substances which he can eat. The plant implies livestock, for many of the crops that grow readily in this country cannot be digested by man who therefore feeds them to animals which produce in return meat, milk, wool, manure and power. Livestock imply a supply of water. Crops and livestock imply the field, which, in turn implies the conversion of natural wilderness to farmland, the provision of field boundaries and commonly some form of drainage as well. The field also implies a range of tools, implements or machines to cultivate and harvest the crops that are grown there. Finally, the need to shelter harvested crops, livestock, field implements, static processing equipment and the men and women concerned with them implies a variety of buildings. Such are the essentials of the farm. As it is in the oldest type of farm to be seen in this country, the reconstructed Iron Age farm on Butser Hill in the Queen Elizabeth Country Park in Hampshire, so it is in the most sophisticated modern farm and in all farms of all ages between them.

The purposes of the farmer have formed or dominated most of the landscape of this country. Indeed, on the land under his control he is responsible for the character and position of nearly everything that lives or stands there. If you wish to see the scope of his achievement, go to the countryside and look around you.

The farmer, however, has not worked alone. He has certainly achieved much with only such resources as local nature thought fit to provide. But from early times he has increasingly sought the aid of technologies and industries beyond the boundaries of the farm, of the village and of the countryside. Many survivals of the past on the farm, therefore, reflect the achievements of industrial developments elsewhere. The industrial archaeology of the farm tells more than an agricultural story. Indeed, it provides a continuous commentary on general economic and technical change.

This book seeks to introduce the reader to the industrial archaeology of farming, which is here rather crudely defined to include all the historical tools and works of the farmer as producer. It seeks to show the scope, content and interest of the subject and to describe, with examples, the various kinds of survivals from the different periods of the past that can still be seen.

No book of this type can be more than an introduction, for the subject is huge and expanding. So is the highly fragmented literature it produces. The writer is only too aware of the inadequacies of his book on so wide a theme and he hopes that readers will help to reduce them by informing him of any examples or publications which should be considered for inclusion in any future edition. But his main hope is that his work will increase the reader's understanding of his agricultural heritage and his pleasure in it by enabling him to learn more about it for himself when he walks or drives in the countryside.

1

The Winning of the Waste

The Manmade Landscape

The agricultural landscape we see around us to-day was formed in many different ways at many different times. But in the beginning all of it was won from primeval wilderness, from moor and scrub on the hills, from forest, heath and fen in the lowlands, from salt marsh and tidal mudflats on the coast. Down the centuries, from Neolithic times until the reign of Victoria, the conversion of the waste to ploughland, pasture and rough grazings has been one of the major tasks of the farmer on whom an increasing population depended for food.

The manmade countryside we have inherited is the greatest of agricultural achievements and nearly all of it was created by men entirely dependent for power on human and animal muscles. Only at the very end of the reclamation did mechanical power make even an occasional contribution. In the 1850s the farmers of the railway age, who made the final attacks on the last strongholds of the ancient waste in southern England, used steam pumps to drain Whittlesey Mere, the only surviving Fenland lake, but they brought Exmoor and Wychwood Forest under cultivation with axe and spade and horse-drawn plough. So the agricultural landscape is a monument to the pre-mechanical age, 'when all things were made by hand and one at a time'. When we look at the countryside of our own time, it is salutary to remember that engineers reckon the strength of a man as one-eighth of a mechanical horse-power.

Physically, much of the story of the winning of the waste is irrecoverably lost, for the process of reclamation inevitably destroys most of the older landscape. In boggy areas, however, the process of clearance can sometimes be traced from the evidence of pollen deposits which record changes in vegetation. For example, palaeobotanical studies show the effects of Cistercian settlement in the twelfth century, the extension of cleared land to make pastures for the sheep of Furness Abbey and the replacement of open grassland by arable crops around Strata Florida Abbey(1). Usually, however, the work of the reclaimers is difficult to follow on the ground unless the area is particularly well documented(2). But much has been learnt from the written record, though inevitably the bulk of continuous documentation concerns recent work and the sources shrink as the centuries recede, and much from the multitude of evidences preserved in the landscape. But the countryside does not readily tell the story of its origins and development. The best preparation for identifying and understanding survivals from the past in farmlands as varied physically and historically as ours is a study of local maps and local records in a local library or museum.

Reclamation from the Forests

In particular, the lowland landscapes, which were for the most part reclaimed from forest and frequently later adapted to changing needs, give no more than hints and clues to their history and little of the older order survives to provide a basis for comparing past and present. The vanished woodlands leave few obvious traces and, for example, the fields, orchards and hopgardens of twentieth-century Kent tell nothing directly about

> '. . . the wooden plough
> Turning the furrows of the first bold field,
> A patch of light, a square of paler green.
> Cupped in the darkness of the Weald . . .
> Thus the foundations of the farm were laid'(3).

The plough and the harrow and the farmer's crops and stock soon obliterate what axe and fire and mattock have left, and most of the primeval wilderness has been farmland for centuries.

The destruction of the Wildwood, the virgin forest of primeval England, began when Neolithic farmers cleared trees and scrub to make their fields and used the woodland around them for grazing their stock. Domesday Book, three thousand years later, recorded an advanced stage in the process and the end probably came in the twelfth century with the conversion of the Forest of Dean, apparently the last approximation to virgin forest to survive, to managed woodland and pasture. The timbers cut from the 71 huge oaks from this forest which Henry III gave to the Dominican friary built at Gloucester between 1241 and 1265, where they can still be seen, are perhaps the last remains above ground of the English Wildwood(4).

Today, after several more centuries of the reclamation of forests already under differing degrees of human exploitation, the verdict is clear. Such areas of ancient forest as survive, though in most cases directly descended from the Wildwood, have all been shaped or influenced by the forester and the farmer(5). The fate of the larger woodland animals provides an historical commentary on the process. The bear became extinct in the tenth century, the beaver in the fourteenth, the wolf in the sixteenth and the wild boar in the seventeenth or eighteenth(6).

Sometimes vanished woodlands have left their outlines on the modern landscape in the form of 'relict' boundary hedges surrounding the fields which were enclosed from them. Thus, the hedge boundaries of Wood Farm at Barrow, Suffolk, preserve 'almost exactly' the boundaries of the wood from which it was reclaimed in Tudor times, while the outline of a 40-acre wood at Little Gransden, Cambridgeshire, which was cleared in 1670, is still identifiable by the thick hedge surrounding the three fields which were formed from it(7). Similarly, Judith's Hedge at Monks Wood Experimental Station, Huntingdonshire – named after the niece of William the Conqueror who was granted land in this area in 1075 – was formerly the boundary of Monks Wood from which it is now separated by fields reclaimed in the seventeenth and eighteenth centuries(8).

On the ground, these former forest areas can often be identified by the woodland plants, such as Dog's Mercury, which they still contain(9). On the map, their irregularity, curves and re-entrants contrast with the more regular and straight-edged fieldboundaries of later date. Their shapes record the work of the peasant reclaimers who, season after season, cut their way around individual large trees or other natural obstacles as they hewed small intakes from the forest. In Oxfordshire, for example, the 'irregular and varying patterns of fields and copses' in the Wychwood area recall the reclamations which in the twelfth and thirteenth centuries established six new settlements in the wild woodland(10). Near Cambridge, Kingston Wood Farm lies within the old Kingston wood whose 'ragged and indented edges still reflect the original clearance in the forest. To stand near the present farmhouse with its home paddocks still largely surrounded by trees is to be in the world of a thousand years ago'(11). Such are the memorials of the peasantry who in generations of forgotten labour converted so much of the lowlands from forests to field and pasture.

Often, however, place-names and field-names are the only clues left. The numerous Wood Farms tell an obvious story but many names are derived from words now forgotten. Thus, the endings '-ley' and '-den' in the Weald area, '-royd' in the north and versions of the Norman-French legal term *assart* mean a clearing in the woodland, the various forms of 'stubbing' or 'roding', 'riding', 'reed' or 'ridding' mean the grubbing out of trees. 'Stocking' is a place of stocks or tree-stumps, and names like Barnet, Brentwood and Brindley or the Norse equivalent, Swithland, denote places of burning(12). More generally, variants of 'breche' refer to newly-broken land and Breach Farm, Burwell, preserves the memory of an area of some 200 acres called 'La Breche' which was enclosed from the waste for cultivation in the thirteenth century(13). Typically, it was through placenames and fieldnames that W.G. Hoskins identified in a Leicestershire parish a black spring mentioned in mediaeval charters but forgotten since the enclosure of 1766, 'jet black on a sunny afternoon, just as the mediaeval peasant saw it when he stooped to drink from it'. From the same source Geoffrey Grigson summoned from the past the ghost of Braydon Forest in Wiltshire which had been farmland for three centuries(14).

Indeed, the reclaimers of the forests have left few memorials of their work save the fields they created and the pattern of the woodlands they spared. This is well illustrated by Wychwood in Oxfordshire, in Saxon times the forest of the Hwicce people whose name it preserves, later a royal hunting forest and finally the scene of the last major woodland reclamation in the country. Under the enclosure Act of 1853 2,000 acres of woodland were allotted to the Crown. They were cleared rapidly and comprehensively and the land was laid out into seven new farms. The first trees were cut in October 1856, the first tenants installed and at work in January 1858. Earlier generations had worked more slowly but the results were the same. For the modern visitor can walk over the Victorian fields without realizing anything of their history unless he happens to see the earthworks at Langley Farm, near Leafield, which are believed to be the remains of King John's forest hunting lodge, or the cast-iron plaque in the farm buildings which commemorates the reclamation(15). The tablet in the church of the significantly named village of Woodhouse Eaves in Leicestershire to the memory of Charles Allsop is probably unique. It commemorates the man who 'by his energy and intelligence and great agricultural knowledge brought a large part of the surrounding district of Charnwood Forest into a high state of cultivation' following the enclosure of 11,000 acres of this huge area of woodland in 1808(16).

Reclamation from Heaths and Uplands
In heathland and upland, too, the achievements of the reclaimers are more obvious than the processes of reclamation. Tennyson's northern farmer, proudly recalling on his deathbed his 'stubbing of Thornaby Waste' and the conversion of bracken and furze 'worth nowt an acre' to good sheep-pasture, grieved that he had not been granted another season

to bring the few remaining acres under cultivation. If he had completed his work he would have left green fields enclosed by stone walls but no record of the manner in which he created them, for the work itself usually left few traces. Thus, in the 1670s 2,245 acres of White Coombs uplands in Cheshire were rented to a group of eleven graziers. By 1750, the area was divided into three farms, each with its own farmstead(17). Such stories can only be recovered in detail from documents, although, as in the lowlands, placenames and fieldnames give general clues and suggestions. Names containing elements of such words as 'down', 'moor', 'fern' or 'bracken' and 'furze' recall past landscapes, names such as Newtake, Newclose or Intake their conversion to farmland(18).

Yet some memorials of such reclamation remain. Indeed, the uplands still preserve traces of 'transhumance', the stage in agricultural exploitation before reclamation, when farmers migrated in summer to the hills where their cattle grazed on the mountain pastures while they themselves lived in a temporary shelter called a 'shieling' in the north of England and a 'hafod' in Wales. Transhumance still continues in some mountainous parts of the mainland of Europe, but in this country the more remote 'summering-houses' have long been abandoned and the less remote converted to permanent farmsteads and the wild pastures around them into fields. In northern England the practice came to an end in the eighteenth century, in Wales it survived into Victorian times, the last recorded summering, in Snowdonia, taking place as late as 1862. The remains of many summering-houses are still visible, as are the marks of stackstands, the dry, level platforms where winter fodder was stored, surrounded by a bank or ditch to keep out the stock. These were built in the eighteenth and nineteenth centuries in the intermediate stage of reclamation when the pastures formerly grazed only in the summer were occupied all the year round.

Again, placenames preserve the memory of the old system. The shepherd's cottage at Batailshieling in the Usway Valley, Northumberland, was originally a shieling which belonged to Henry Bataille in the thirteenth century. The Norse element 'erg', meaning summer pastures, is found in Hawkshead, which was once Hawkr's shieling, and in Sholver, which was once Skolg's shieling. Hafod occurs frequently in the placenames of the upland parishes of Wales and part of Beddgelert Forest is called Hafod Fawr, the big hafod, from a farm of that name which was once a true hafod. Similarly, 'booth' in Derbyshire and Lancashire probably recalls the summer settlements of herdsmen which later became permanent farms(19).

The most obvious and dramatic relics of upland reclamation, however, are the miles of stone walls which recall both the labour and the progress of the reclaiming farmer as he brought the bleak and desolate hills under varying degrees of agricultural control. (These walls are described in Chapter 2.)

In the lowlands, the poor, sandy heaths were among the least rewarding soils and consequently were only reclaimed after the more fertile land had been brought into cultivation and then only by those who could find no better land to win and farm. Typically, much of the light land of Lindsey Heath in Lincolnshire was not enclosed until the time of George III, more than a century after most of the better soils around it had been divided into fields(20). The processes of reclamation of such areas by peasants and squatters have left few marks on the landscape. On Holton Heath in Dorset, it is true, enclosures dug by peasants in the sixteenth and seventeenth centuries are still visible as low, broken banks. So are the low banks 'stretching endlessly' across West Parsley Heath in the same country which were built in the seventeenth century to divide this land, too poor to cultivate but valuable for grazing and turf-cutting, among claimants(21). But these are exceptional.

Indeed, the peasant reclamations in upland and lowland are difficult to follow except by detailed local study in the library and on the ground. Most are now part of the farming system, though a few identifiable achievements survive on the high hills, abandoned when the tide of cultivation receded. Perhaps the most remarkable of these are the ruins of Fernacre Farm, on Bodmin Moor, first recorded in 1327, and 'the shadowy outlines of mediaeval fields long washed over by a sea of bracken' high in the wastes of the Moor, the work of peasant-colonists in the days of land-hunger before the Black Death(22).

On the other hand the reclamations by the great landowners, who in the eighteenth and early nineteenth centuries continued in the uplands the tradition of the monastic sheepfarmers after most of the lowlands had been brought under cultivation, have left stories that can be read by all who run or walk or drive. The landlord-created landscape of Northumberland, a product of the long Hanoverian peace, is probably the most spectacular memorial to these men(23). The orderly countryside of fields, woods, roads and farmsteads, won mainly from desolate moorland, which are the legacy of Sir William Loraine of Kirkdale, Horace St Paul of Glendale, Lord Delaval of Ford and their colleagues are paralleled by the achievements of the Sykes on the Lincolnshire Wolds and other reclaimers elsewhere(24). The work of all these pioneers changed the face of much of the countryside and culminated, in mid-Victorian times, in the conversion to farmland by the Knights of 20,000 acres of unenclosed Exmoor, the last great reclaimable area of wilderness in south-western England(25).

Nevertheless, the most haunting relic of the gradual conquest of the more difficult and demanding areas of waste in this country recalls not the power and purpose of the wealthy landowner but the tenacity and effort of the peasant. John Hooper made the last new farm on Dartmoor about 1870, living in a makeshift shelter of rocks and rushes while he built his cottage and outbuildings, and reclaimed some 30 acres for his fields. Nuns Cross Farm is now abandoned, a silent reminder of the end of a tradition going back to Neolithic times, for Hooper was probably the last man in England to win farmland as generations of his peasant-ancestors had won it: creating his own farm with his own hands from the unclaimed wilderness(26).

Reclamation from the Sea

The most striking monuments to historical reclamations are the embankments, artificial waterways and pumping systems by which land was recovered and held from the sea and from inland waters. Some of the multitude of schemes of which these formed part were large, some small, some earned a place in national history, some were of only minor importance, some were completed in a few years, some were the work of more than one generation or more than one century, some were achieved by local resources, some depended on men and skills imported from other countries who left their name to the Dutch River in Yorkshire and the results of their craft in many areas besides the Fenlands(27). The contribution of all these schemes to the agricultural landscape was immense.

The rich alluvial soil of tidal flats has inspired many 'innings', as the enclosure of mudflats is called, along different areas of coastline. Their stories are often preserved by the earthworks which recovered land from the sea and, less dramatically, by the occasional survival of the hollow treetrunk pipes which were used to drain the innings at low tide and were plugged at high tide(28). Thus, the series of seawalls along the Wash, many now converted to roads, which stand several feet above the surrounding land and 'hardly ever run straight for any distance but all the time seem to be going somewhere'(29) record the winning of tens of thousands of acres of rich land over many centuries(30). A literal landmark in the process, which by 1800 had added a recognized agricultural area to Lincolnshire, is the so-called 'Roman Wall'. This bank probably marks the seaward limit of reclamation in the late Middle Ages and includes the appropriately named Seafield at Leverington, north-west of Wisbech(31). Seafield is now ten miles from the coast and between the sea and the 'Roman Wall' lie a succession of later walls ending, for the time being at least, with the Jubilee Wall completed in 1977.

Less spectacularly, embankments along the Clyst in Devon protect 'the rich and level pastures interlaced with the blue veins of ditches' won by William Sukespice and his descendants between Angevin and Victorian times, and few holidaymakers in this popular area realize that the green fields which stretch from Alphington to Powderham were once the salt marshes of an estuary well over a mile wide at Topsham. The red cliff to which the tides crept can still be seen at Millbury Farm, Exminster(32). Indeed, many river-mouths and low-lying coastal areas show examples of this form of reclamation. One such innings aroused the passionate concern of that most improbable of field-makers, Shelley. In 1812 he encouraged his friend William Madocks, who had already received a gold medal from the Board of Agriculture for inning a thousand acres of tidal mud, to complete the embankment which reclaimed 300 acres of saltings from the estuary of the Traeth by Porthmadog. Predictably, his enthusiasm, which at first caused his wife to complain that he was in the office from morning to night, was shortlived. But the work endures and now carries the coastal road and railway(33).

Few schemes, however, have earned more than a reference in local histories to the changes they have wrought in local geography, although their total effect has been considerable. For example, embankers beginning in monastic times, or possibly earlier, secured the Caldicot Levels in Monmouthshire(34); left a period piece of mediaeval landscape in the chessboard pattern of ditched fields behind the Pevensey seawall(35); caused the migration of the Norfolk village of Cley to a new coastline won in the early seventeenth century, leaving the church a mile from the sea(36); near the mouth of the Humber converted Sunk Island to mainland fields and Patrington Haven to an inland hamlet by the end of the eighteenth century(37); and created much of Foulness and Canvey Island by a series of innings, many of which can still be traced(38).

The most dramatic of all these works was undoubtedly the inning of Romney Marsh, once a huge shallow bay, now a level pasture traditionally carrying more sheep to the acre than any similar area in the world. The reclamation began early, for some 24,000 acres, nearly half the final area of made land, were won before the end of the Roman period, when a natural shingle bank stretching far out into the shallow sea was reinforced and joined with a six-mile embankment, now called the Rhee Wall, to form a huge triangle which the sea could not enter. The work was later continued by the monks of Canterbury and then by local landowners, among them the descendants of Sir Richard Guldeford who inned the level that bears his name and in 1505 built the church at East Guldeford, a mile east of Rye. The reclamation was finally completed in 1838, when the saltings below the walls of Rye, including much of the old Cinque Port harbour, were enclosed. Many of the seawalls of the old innings can still be traced and the visitor can stand on the road which runs along the Rhee Wall where Thomas à Becket probably once stood with a cloak over his finery, a map in his hand and his bailiffs around him, and planned the advance beyond the wall which is still called the Innings of St Thomas. But where he saw glistening mud, his modern successor will see only fields, for the sea is now three miles away(39).

The interpretation of the works left by these innings, however, requires considerable local and historical knowledge. Fortunately detailed guides for two typical areas are available. South Lincolnshire has been the subject of a comprehensive study undertaken 'to explain the impressive sea and fen dykes which the traveller who leaves the main road through the Lincolnshire fenlands can see traversing the open countryside for many miles'(40). Similarly, a historical survey of the Dengie Marshes in Essex has identified and recorded the different innings, the generations of the seawalls, the irregular early fields preserving the pattern of the creeks

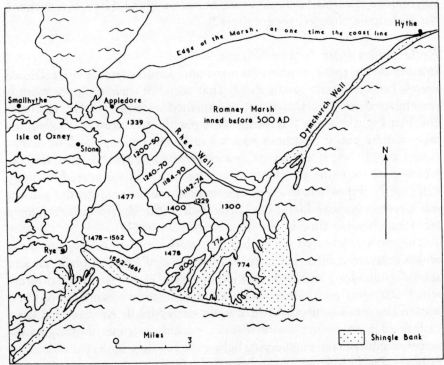

Map of the reclamations of Romney Marsh to the end of the seventeenth century. Today Oxney is an isle in name only and Rye is two miles from the sea. (Based upon a map in *Romney Marsh* by W.J.C. Murray, 1953, and a map by James Elliot, 'sometime engineer of Romney Marsh', 1873, in Stone-cum-Oxney church)

which once dissected the saltings, the later rectangular enclosures, the raised mediaeval causeways where sheep could take refuge if the sea breached the embankments, and the lanes along which carts once carried farm produce to barges(41). It is worth remembering, when walking along the remains of old innings, that a modest bank three feet high, six feet broad at the base and two feet broad at the top contains one and a half tons of earth for every yard of its length.

The Humber area provides interesting examples of 'warping', another method of winning land from the sea. This allows the tides which flow up the estuary to cover selected areas of land and deposit silt when the movement of the waters is checked by artificial banks. Around Yokefleet and Blacktoft on the north coast of the Humber, where the warping drains run three miles inland, this practice continued until 1950 and a number of the field banks which retained the water can still be seen. South of the estuary the same system achieved a more conspicuous success by converting over the generations the fens that originally surrounded the Isle of Axholme into rich ploughland. Here, as elsewhere, the reclaimers changed geography(42).

Reclamation from Inland Waters

Inland, down the centuries, farmers and landowners have reclaimed meres, bogs and fens so effectively that some of their drainage work is remembered only by the names of vanished wetlands. Oslac, Draymer and Flat Pightle in the Cambridgeshire parish of Foxton recall a muddy lake, a mere and a peatmoss which had become ploughland by Stuart times; a reedy bog at Soham in Cambridgeshire betrays the site of the lake which gave its name to 'the farm by the lake' and supported a fishery sufficiently important to earn references in mediaeval records; and the more recent Newland field on Adrian Bell's Suffolk farm was reclaimed from marsh some time in the nineteenth century(43).

The most celebrated of all drainage works in the country are those which converted into rich farmland the flooded Fenland plain, an area some 70 miles long and 30 miles wide south and east of the Wash through which six rivers and numerous minor streams once meandered on their way to the sea. The process began in the early Middle Ages and has left a variety of monuments and evidences, including some of the greatest achievements of civil engineering before the building of the canals and the railways. First came the local schemes of colonizing monks and peasants. These were followed by more ambitious undertakings to improve substantial areas by a form of ditching, even as a farmer ditches marshy meadows. But here the ditches which straightened old watercourses or created new ones, and thus made possible the more direct and rapid fall of the waters to the outlets on the coast, were artificial rivers, their lengths measured in miles, their widths in yards.

The earliest of these schemes was Morton's Leam, cut by Henry VII's great minister in the 1480s, which still runs for 12 miles between Peterborough and Guyhirn to speed the flow of the River Nene. The next major work, Popham's Eau, was cut in 1609 by a company under Sir John Popham to carry water from a tributary of the Nene to the Ouse. This served as a prologue to the more comprehensive schemes of the Bedford Level Corporation, founded in 1631 under the fourth Earl of Bedford and the famous engineer, Cornelius Vermuyden, which in the next generation reclaimed vast areas of southern Fenland. Much of Vermuyden's work still patterns and drains the fens, notably the seven miles of the New South Eau, the nine miles of the Sixteen Foot Drain, the ten miles of the Forty Foot Drain and, above all, the twenty-one miles of the Old Bedford River, which he cut in 1637. A whole new landscape was thus won for farming.

All was not straightforward, for these gigantic ditches and those which followed them brought new problems which required new forms of engineering to control them. The reclaimed peatland gradually shrank, partly through drying, partly through bacterial action, until the fields were below the level of the rivers into which their ditches had originally drained. So man-made riverwalls replaced riverbanks and gravity could no longer drain the new lands. From the early seventeenth century, therefore, wind-driven pumps were used to raise water from the field ditches and discharge it into the increasingly embanked rivers. Yet the level of the soil still fell and, despite technical improvements in the windmills and the use of systems of double-lift or treble-lift whereby two or even three mills raised in stages the water for which formerly one had been sufficient, the waters steadily gained. By the eighteenth century the whole huge reclamation was facing disaster and the ultimate abandonment of the Fens was freely discussed.

The memory of these troubled times is preserved in semicircular bends in otherwise straight riverwalls which mark the sites of repairs to embankments which failed and broke as the peat on which they stood shrank. But the engineer of the steam age came to the rescue just in time. In 1817 the first steam-driven pump was installed in the Fenlands and soon a score of engines were pumping into the rivers the water with which the windmills had struggled in vain. The remains of the various generations of Fenland pump and prime mover, the windmill, the steam engine, the diesel engine and the electric engine, belong to the industrial archaeology of engineering rather than of farming. But, like the field machinery in the museums, they bear witness to the debt of the farmer to the engineer.

The most obvious and impressive works in the Fenlands are the great artificial rivers and their associated drainage systems. These are so well documented that 'almost every drain and watercourse [in the Fens] can be dated and its original purpose and its countless alterations understood . . . The jigsaw of drains falls into a complete and magnificent picture of man's conquest of nature'(44). Another group of survivals are the early pumping installations(45). To-day only one late, small and by no means typical example of the 400 windpumps which served the Fenlands in the early nineteenth century can be seen, although the remains of four others survive and a number of sites can be identified by traces of drains or reservoirs(46). Time has dealt a little less harshly with the 70 steam engines which were installed between 1817 and 1880. Three engines and a number of engine houses still stand(47) and their former importance is pleasingly commemorated on a plaque on the house of the Hundred Foot Engine erected by the Drainage Commissioners of the Littleport and Downham District in 1830,

'These fens have oft times been by water drowned.
Science a remedy in water found.
The power of steam, she said, shall be employed
And the destroyer by itself destroyed'(48).

None of these engines is now working. From the 1920s onwards they were gradually replaced by diesel engines which are now, in turn, being replaced by electric power, so that the diesel engines themselves are becoming material for the industrial archaeologist(49).

One of the triumphs of the steam age was the drainage of Whittlesey Mere, the last of the lakes of the primeval Fenland, in 1852. The impeller of the pump, which William Wells used in this reclamation is now in the Science Museum, London, very appropriately, since he first saw the pump at the Great Exhibition in 1851(50). He also left an informative memorial, the Holme Post, near the site of the mere to record the shrinkage of the peat after drainage. This cast iron post, which was taken from the Crystal Palace when it was dismantled in Hyde Park in 1851, was driven into the ground, about one mile north of Holme in Huntingdonshire, its top flush with the level of the peat. By 1860 nearly five feet of the post were exposed, by 1892 ten feet, and to-day nearly thirteen feet are above ground(51).

A curious legacy of this reclamation is a group of several blocks of roughly cut masonry, the largest probably weighing nearly a ton, at Engine Farm, about a mile north-east of Ramsey St Mary in Huntingdonshire. These originally formed a stone islet in the mere and are believed to have been intended for Ramsey Abbey and jettisoned when the boat carrying them across the lake ran aground. After the drainage of the mere they were moved to their present site. Similar stones by the nearby pumping station and by the Old Nene were probably part of similar cargoes(52).

A modern Fenland map gives further clues to the process of reclamation. The Isle of Ely, like the Isle of Axholme, is no longer an island; Welshes Dam on the Old Bedford River is named after Edmund Welsh, a seventeenth-century drainage contractor; French Drove and French Farm in Thorney recall Huguenots who settled there; and Adventurers Fen was the share of newly drained land allocated to investors who had 'adventured' their money in the project. This method of financing such work was first developed in the early seventeenth century and was the basis of most later Fenland drainage, including the schemes of the Bedford Level Corporation(53). Then, too, the pattern of settlement preserves a memory of the undrained wilderness, for the silt beds and banks of the old rivers, called roddons, provided more stable soil for the builder than the surrounding peatland. Consequently many farmsteads and other buildings are sited along the lines of these forgotten watercourses(54).

The scope and effects of the Fenland reclamation have tended to overshadow the varied achievements of the drainer elsewhere. But these, too, have been considerable. Thus, the derelict windmills of the Broadland, which mostly date from the nineteenth century but often replaced earlier ones, provide another example of the use of mechanical power in the reclamation and maintenance of farmland. In 1920 there were over 60 such mills at work in the area and the last of them, which stands at Ashtree Farm on the Bure, ceased work as recently as 1953(55). Again, the Hull valley, once a desolation of swamps, meres and salt marshes, shows the lines of the monastic and later drainage schemes, notably the drains authorized by an act of Parliament of 1798, which have converted it to ploughland and pasture(56).

On the other side of the country, the story of the draining of the 250 square miles of the Somerset Levels covers 1000 years of human effort and includes the first reference in English history to a drainage specialist, Girard Fossarius, who appears in Domesday Book as a tenant of Glastonbury Abbey which was responsible for so much of the earlier reclamation. It has left a series of embankments, cuts and ditch systems, notably the Lake Wall built round Sowy in the thirteenth century and the Pillrow Cut of the same period and, latterly, pumping stations, although many of the older works have probably been modified by later improvements. It has also, incidentally, destroyed the topography of Sedgemoor, the last English battlefield. The Black Dyke which

Monmouth's men followed in their advance through the peatmoor mists of the July night in 1685 is now part of a larger drainage scheme. Both the fatal Langmoor Rhine, where their splashing sent a royal trooper galloping back to his comrades 'calling . . . "Beat your drums, the enemy is come"', so losing them their advantage of surprise, and the Bussex Rhine which ended their advance and lost them the battle, have now disappeared(57).

The drainage of the peatmosses of Lancashire and Cheshire, which began in the seventeenth century and ended in late Victorian times, was less dramatic. But here, too, drainers changed the map. Their most spectacular achievement was the clearance of Martin Mere behind Southport. This lake, some three miles long and two miles wide, is said to have given the common Lancashire name of Rimmer to those who lived around its edge. The sluice which Thomas Fleetwood, the squire of Bank Hall, cut in 1692 from the lake to an outfall to the sea at Cossens can still be seen, although it was not until the nineteenth century that the lake bottom was finally converted to 'an area of rich black soil and huge rectangular fields which is one of the most important potato growing regions of the area'(58). The traces of allotments created in 1764 after the drainage of part of Chat Moss are one relic of the moss drainage(59). Others are the occasional cottages of clay and thatch which were the temporary homes of the first tenants who leased acreages of raw moss after the landowner had cut the main drains and then completed the work by cutting secondary ditches and slowly converting their spongy soil to cropland(60).

The mosses, however, were the last great triumph of the large-scale drainer, although as late as 1830 the drainage of Peakirk Moor and Newborough Fen in Northamptonshire made possible the building of the village of Newborough on a previously empty site(61). Ironically, one of the last substantial drainage schemes of the nineteenth century resulted from the work of previous drainers, for the serious floods around Oxford in 1825 were ascribed partly to the increasing volume of water reaching the Thames. One of the purposes of the drainage works of the 1850s, which created 'a sort of Bampton polderland' between the Oxfordshire villages of Newbridge and Radcot, was to control flood-water, but it also allowed the more intensive use of a considerable area of riverside meadow(62).

Deerparks, Decoys and Warrens

In their different ways the use of land for deerparks, decoys and warrens preserved or exploited the resources of the waste. Consequently their stories and legacies provide an interesting commentary on the process of reclamation which gradually converted all but a few to farmland.

Deerparks became a feature of the countryside in the early Middle Ages, when the steady progress of reclamation increasingly separated manor and village from the shrinking Wildwood(63). They were created by local lords, who enclosed an area of the waste and the wild animals that lived in it primarily for hunting but also as a source of fresh meat. We owe the survival of the wild white cattle to their enclosure in mediaeval times, hence their present name of White Park cattle. The formation of such parks required a royal licence and seems to have been regarded as 'a rich man's privilege and a not-so-rich man's status symbol'(64), though they served the tables as well as the pride of the owners. Historically, they were a means of preserving certain of the amenities and benefits of the disappearing wilderness. Agriculturally, they can be described as a primitive form of ranching.

These parks, which contained a mixture of woodland and rough grazing, were commonly enclosed by a ditch and a bank topped with a fence of wooden palings. They varied greatly in size – some were 100 acres or less in extent, one no more than 30 acres, and others two or three miles in diameter. Their total number was considerable and it has been estimated that there was, on average, one every 15 square miles(65).

The work of the farmer caused such parks to be created. The demands of the farmer eventually caused their disappearance. As increasing population made corn and cattle more profitable than sport and venison the creation of new parks ceased and, one by one, existing parks were converted to farmland, mostly, it seems, in Tudor and Stuart times, though some survived as amenity grounds to be improved by Capability Brown and his colleagues.

To-day Staverton Park in East Suffolk, Sutton Coldfield Park near Birmingham, Moccas in Herefordshire, which preserves its pale fence, and Bannoc near Lostwithiel give some idea of a mediaeval deerpark, while Hatfield Forest in Essex, 'almost certainly unique in England and possibly in the world', still contains very many of the elements from which deerparks were created – coppice woods, timber trees and scrub, grassland, deer, cattle and also a rabbit warren. Elsewhere vanished deerparks have left as relics only boundary ditches, banks, hedges and such placenames as Lawn Field, recalling the open areas where deer grazed, and Park Farm and Palegates Farm. Many week-end walkers in London's green belt know the pleasant countryside around King's Langley in Hertfordshire, the site of a mediaeval royal palace for which Chaucer was for a time clerk of the works. Few, however, are aware of the imprint of the deerpark in which the palace once stood. A footpath marks one of its boundaries, and the large fields into which it was divided in the seventeenth century contrast strikingly with the small fields around it created by piecemeal enclosure. Incidentally, one of these large fields retained into the nineteenth century the name of Cains, which is derived from Camylesland, the area of the royal park which supplied fodder for the camel which Edward I received as a gift from an eastern ruler(66).

Deerparks preserved a natural resource threatened by the axe of the reclaimer, decoy ponds to attract and catch ducks and other wildfowl preserved a natural resource threatened by the spade of the embanker and drainer. In the seventeenth century, the draining of the Fens was followed by the construction there of a new type of decoy introduced from Holland into which the birds were not driven but enticed. In the nineteenth century 14 such decoys were built in the Somerset Levels to continue in new form the trade of the old fowlers whose wild hunting areas had been converted to farmland. But most of the 200 or so decoys in the country stood on the former marshes and mudflats of south-east England. Thus, the reclaimed Dengie Marshes in Essex, included three decoy ponds among their fields. This curious relic of the food-gathering tradition could not, however, withstand the rural depression of late Victorian times. Apparently none of the Fenland decoys, and only six of the Somerset ones, were in use at the end of the nineteenth century and the last of the 31 in Essex was abandoned early in the present century. To-day only a few survive (67).

The deerpark and the decoy were artificial prolongations of the past. The man-made warren, on the other hand, was a new form of enterprise, for the rabbit only established itself in this country after the Norman Conquest and warrens were unknown before the early Middle Ages. The warrens were often enclosed by banks or walls and frequently contained artificial pits or artificial mounds called pillowmounds which were sometimes over 100 feet long and 20 feet wide. Since plentiful rabbits and good crops are incompatible, warrens were normally limited to areas remote from cultivation, where for centuries they provided the farmer with one of his most effective ways of exploiting heath and unreclaimed upland.

Inevitably such a form of production could not survive the waste on which it depended, and the reclamations of the eighteenth and early nineteenth centuries ended the man-managed warren. In Bedfordshire and Lincolnshire they had disappeared by the 1840s, in the East Riding of Yorkshire in the next decade, although they survived in Norfolk until late Victorian times and on Dartmoor until after the Second World War. The agricultural depression of the late nineteenth century brought a temporary revival of interest in this form of enterprise, and a few new warrens were established on land where no other form of production was then economic. They succumbed, however, to the competition of imported rabbit meat

1 A shieling on Whitelyne Common, above Bewcastle in Cumberland. It was one of a group of shielings, probably established in the Middle Ages, which were abandoned some time before the middle of the eighteenth century.

2 Once all this area at the mouth of the Great Ouse was tidal mud. From mediaeval times onwards farmers have converted thousands of acres of saltings on the coasts of the Wash to farmland by 'inning'. The fields nearest the camera are now in normal cultivation, though the curving boundaries of some of them preserve the marks of the wandering creeks of the old marshes. On the other side of the river a more recently 'inned' area is being drained and will later be ploughed and cropped.

3   A wooden drainage pipe, made from a hollowed tree trunk, with one end open and the other fitted with a plug, formerly used by farmers to control the waterlevel on land reclaimed from the Kent and Sussex marshes. It probably dates from the Middle Ages.

4   One of Vermuyden's drainage cuts in the Fenlands. The Forty Foot Drain near Chatteris.

5   Three generations of Fenland drainage pumps. The windmill probably dates from the eighteenth century. The steam pump was built in the 1840s. In the white building between them stands a diesel engine installed in 1926. Today a fourth prime mover, electricity, secures the Fenlands.

6 Most rabbit warrens have long been converted into fields, but a number of their remains survive on Dartmoor. These 'pillowmounds' formed part of Huntingdon Warren, about fifteen miles south-east of Lydford.

7 The 'business end' of a reconstructed ard, the primitive form of plough which broke but did not overturn the soil.

8 By the end of the Middle Ages most of the workable land in the country had been reclaimed. But the high tide of cultivation later receded, leaving only the outlines of abandoned fields. Some of this marginal land, however, was reclaimed again during the Second World War. This picture shows fields of both types on the slopes of Dartmoor.

9   Outlines of Iron Age fields on the Wiltshire Downs. These were formed by cross-ploughing with the ard.

10   Some of these fields on the Penwith Peninsula, near Zennor in Cornwall, were probably formed in the Bronze Age and the Iron Age and the massive stone walls which divide them were built from the granite boulders cleared from the land at the original reclamation.

11 The last of the open field villages, Laxton in Nottinghamshire. All the farmsteads stand in the village and the farmers go out every day to work in the surrounding fields, part of which can be seen in the background.

12 The only open field parish left in England, Laxton in Nottinghamshire. Two of the three open fields surrounded by enclosed fields can be seen in the centre of the photograph. The village of Laxton stands in the left middle distance, with the third open field behind it.

13   A typical open field village in the Middle Ages. The field in the foreground is the fallow field. As livestock are allowed to graze on the stubbles and weeds of this field, the two other fields, one carrying winter-sown corn, the other spring-sown corn and legumes, are protected by temporary fencing. This diorama is in the Science Museum.

14   Harvesting in the 1940s in the only open fields which survive in this country. The strips of the individual farmers are separated only by furrows. The empty stubbles, the waiting sheaves and the working harvesters show the different stages of the harvest reached by different farmers.

15   The fields of Padbury, Buckinghamshire, showing the open field strips, preserved as ridge-and-furrow, on which the hedged field system was imposed by the enclosure of 1796. The road shown runs midway between Grange Farm, which can be seen in the left hand corner of the photograph, and Hedges Farm. See page 48.

16   Three ages of field system in Oxfordshire. The small, squarish enclosures visible as crop marks are Iron Age fields. The furrows continuing across the modern field from the allotments on the right and those parallel with them are the strips of a mediaeval open field. The modern fields were probably enclosed in the time of George III.

17 The curved furrows ploughed by mediaeval ox-teams in the open fields of the Vale of Pickering have been 'fossilized' and preserved in the field-system created by the enclosures. The curved S-furrows were formed as the ploughmen manoeuvred their teams of eight oxen yoked in pairs for easier turning on the headlands.

18 Lynchets at Winterbourne Steepleton, Dorset. Such cultivation terraces were ploughed by land-hungry farmers in many different ages in many different parts of the country. Many are mediaeval, the highwater marks of cultivation by peasants striving to feed their growing villages in the days before the Black Death.

and fur and the trapping and shooting by farmers permitted by the Ground Game Act of 1880. To-day all that remains of this system of meat-production is the occasional site which has not been ploughed into oblivion, warreners' houses at Thetford, Norfolk, Mildenhall, Suffolk, and Hatfield Forest, and the names of various Warren Farms or Coney Farms(68).

2

Fields and Field Systems

The Oldest Fields

The first step in reclamation is the clearance or drainage of the waste. The second is the division of the new-won farmland into manageable fields.

The oldest fields to have left traces above ground are the so-called 'Celtic' or 'prehistoric' fields which date from the Bronze Age, the Iron Age or Roman times. These are the small enclosures, squarish or roughly rectangular in shape and generally between a third of an acre and two acres, which survive as grassgrown outlines, mainly in chalk and limestone areas. Originally such fields covered large areas of the lowlands, but most of them have been destroyed by later cultivation, many in the ploughing campaign during and after the Second World War. Areas of these ancient fields are still visible, however, in various parts of the country, including, appropriately, a number on the downs above the reconstruction of an Iron Age farm at Butser Hill in Queen Elizabeth Country Park, Hampshire, while aerial photography can reveal traces where nothing can be seen on the ground(1).

These little fields were created by the action of the *ard*, the light, primitive plough, no more than a pointed stick pulled through the soil by animals or men, which only scratched the surface of the soil. Consequently, it was necessary to make a second row of scratches at right angles to the first to secure a proper tilth, and this tended to produce a squarish field. No fragments of ards have been unearthed in Britain, but sufficient remains have been found on the Continent to make possible the reconstruction of this implement. Various plough marks formed by ards, however, have been found in this country. The oldest, discovered in soil below a burial mound near Avebury, dates from *c.* 3000 BC and this 'series of minute grooves running at right angles to each other and so forming a crisscross pattern' is the first recognizable field in England(2).

The oldest fields still farmed were probably contemporary with some of these grassgrown enclosures and older thàn many of them. It is almost certain that the network of small, squarish fields on the Penwith peninsula, near Zennor in Cornwall, was formed in the Bronze Age and the Iron Age and that the massive walls which divide them were built from the granite boulders cleared off the land in the original reclamation(3). The men who made these fields were, therefore, the first of the multitude of nameless farmers whose labours created the pattern of the agricultural landscape we have inherited.

Some of these early fields may have formed part of the primitive agricultural system called infield-outfield, in which the infield area near the village or homestead remained in regular cultivation while patches of the more distant outfield were cropped from time to time on a shifting cultivation basis and then abandoned to recuperate for a period before being ploughed again. Centuries ago growth of population made necessary the gradual conversion of outfields to permanent ploughland or pasture and they have left few traces on the landscape except such relics as 'the sweeping curves of walling' at Towednack in Cornwall which was once the boundary of a vanished outfield(4). The system however, was known in the sandy Brecklands of East Anglia as recently as Stuart and Hanoverian times, and its signs are still preserved there in the field pattern(5).

Early Enclosed Fields

All other surviving fields were formed not by the ard but by the mouldboard plough, which was known in this country at least by Roman times and which we still use. This cuts the soil horizontally with the share, vertically with the coulter and overturns it by sliding it along the curved surface of the mouldboard, thus making possible without cross-ploughing a deeper and better seedbed than the ard can achieve. But it needs more animal power to pull it and is more difficult for the ploughman to lift and turn. Once the mouldboard ploughman has started a furrow, therefore, he is anxious to keep his team on the move for a reasonable distance intead of wasting time and effort in stopping and turning unnecessarily. So the new kind of plough created a new kind of field, one considerably larger and more elongated than that created by and for the ard.

The fields created and worked by Saxon and mediaeval pioneers with their mouldboard ploughs varied immensely in size, purpose and relationship to other fields. But essentially they all belong to two main types: individual fields enclosed by hedge, wall or ditch, and various forms of 'open field'.

The individual fields were shaped, one at a time, by individual farmers establishing their farms in the wilderness. Their main characteristics are their small size and irregular outlines, for they were formed by men who worked seasonally and piecemeal in such time as they could spare from the cultivation of fields already secured, and who took their field-boundaries around large trees, boulders or boggy patches too difficult to clear that year. Many of these fields have been replanned or amalgamated with other fields, but others survive and a few can be identified from the record of their origins. Around Belsize in Northamptonshire, for example, the small fields with twists and turns in their boundaries and the irregularly shaped patches in the woodlands recall the thirteenth century colonization of this forest area(6). More specifically, Knapwell Wood Farm, south of Knapwell village in Cambridgeshire, was once an isolated settlement in the woods, first recorded in 1278, and its three fields, totalling only 15 acres, are probably those originally reclaimed. Similarly, at Corscombe Court in Dorset the northward view of small fields bounded by large banks with thickly wooded hedgerows shows a landscape little changed since it was established by clearing the forest in the thirteenth century or earlier(7). Rookery Farm at Monewden in Suffolk provides a more recent instance. The farmhouse was built in 1593, possibly on land recently reclaimed from forest, and a map of 1656 shows the small fields around it 'corresponding very closely to the hedge pattern today'(8). In Wales the process of fieldmaking can sometimes be followed in the fieldnames which show the spread of cultivation from the single farmstead which was so typical of Welsh settlement, the 'field in front of the house' and the 'hayfield' to the 'new field' or the 'mountain field' most recently won from the wasteland(9). The enclosed field has a long history and there are many ancient fields among the later creations in the modern hedged and walled landscape.

Farms and estates were also enclosed, and a number of hedges, banks and ditches which once bounded ancient properties can still be traced. Some survive from early Saxon times. The double hedgebank between the parishes of Cadbury and Stockleigh Pomeroy in Devon, for example, once marked the western edge of the estate of Cada and probably dates from the beginning of Saxon settlement in this area in the seventh century. In Cadbury parish the ancient bank which marked the boundary of the lord's farm still shows the care with which he secured a water supply for his cattle – it stands a few feet on the further side of the local stream running by his farmstead(10). Such enclosures record the decisions of farmers as well as the territories of magnates.

The Open Fields and their Enclosure

The early enclosed fields were made by individual peasants and farmed by the reclaimer and his successors however they wished. The open fields, on the other hand, were part of a system under communal control. The origins of the system are uncertain, but in its thousand years of history it occurred in a wide variety of forms and stages of development over large areas of the country, mostly in the midlands, the south and the east(11). To-day it is gone, leaving in the whole of the country only one working example, at Laxton in Nottinghamshire, and a number of scattered traces.

In crudely diagrammatic and necessarily over-simplified terms, this system, as exemplified at Laxton, comprised three large arable areas bounded by hedges, walls or fences and divided legally, but not by any substantial barrier, into a number of small strips. Each of these strips was cultivated by an individual farmer who might farm any number of these small 'fields' in different parts of the large fields.

The cropping of these three arable areas of ploughland, from whose lack of internal divisions the system derives its name, was determined by communal law and custom. Typically, it followed a rotation of a wintersown corncrop, springsown crops, mostly corn but perhaps including beans or peas, and a fallow which allowed the land to recuperate and farmers to control weeds by cultivation and grazing. Detailed regulations allowed farmers to turn their stock into the open fields when they were not carrying crops, to graze on stubbles and weeds and also on the grass of any banky or marshy unploughed land the fields contained. In addition, each farmer was allotted a share of the meadowland where he cut hay, after which the meadow was thrown open for grazing, and also grazing rights on the village green and other commons, which were often of considerable extent.

There were, of course, endless variations of the system, with different numbers of fields and different sequences of cropping as well as considerable changes in particular systems in the course of their long history. But essentially the open field farm consisted of a number of scattered strips in the arable fields, the right to cut hay in the meadowland and the right to graze stock on the ploughland after the crops had been harvested, on the meadow after the hay had been cut and on the commons(12).

The system ended with the extinction of the grazing rights over the open fields and the reallocation of the scattered ploughland strips to make compact areas under individual occupation which were then formed into the type of field with which we are familiar. This was often accompanied by the ending of the grazing rights over meadows, greens and commons, which were also divided among individual occupiers and formed into fields. These changes, which altered the face of so much of our landscape, are called enclosures, since land formerly open was converted into a pattern of enclosed fields. The word is convenient, for it records obvious physical change, but enclosures of open field land were undertaken for different reasons in different ways at different periods. The number and variety of traces left by the open fields and their associated pastures, and the means whereby they were converted into other forms of field system, reflect the scope and importance of this major theme in our agricultural history(13).

Enclosures of open field holdings were known in the Middle Ages, but the first general stage in the process of change was the enclosure movement of the fifteenth and sixteenth centuries which converted ploughland to hedged pastures for the more profitable sheep. These enclosures left their mark on the landscape, as well as in Tudor pamphlet literature and statute book. At Clapton in Cambridgeshire, the rectangular fields of 10 to 15 acres into which the lawyer, John Fisher, divided 1000 acres of open fields in 1489 can still be seen. At Lamport, in Northamptonshire, the enclosures of areas of open fields made in the 1570s by John Isham, mercer and merchant adventurer, can be traced through the continuance of the names he gave his new fields. Some appear in nineteenth century records and one, Colcot Close, survives to this day as Corkcutt Close(14). Enclosure of this type apparently declined with decreasing economic incentives in Elizabethan times, but enclosure continued during the following 150 years on a smaller scale and, therefore, in a less dramatic fashion.

Sometimes a general enclosure was made by the lord of the manor, as at Ragdale in Leicestershire in 1628. Sir Henry Shirley enclosed the open fields there and left a landscape, which survives with little outward change, of 'tall hedgerows wriggling into the distance' and wide expanses of unbroken pasture still faintly marked by the ridge-and-furrow of the old ploughlands(15). Sometimes there was limited, piecemeal enclosure by agreement among farmers who found it convenient to consolidate their holdings of dispersed strips by purchase or exchange and then enclose them into individually occupied fields. For example, at Great Shelford in Cambridgeshire *c.* 1500 and at Grassington in Yorkshire a century later, villagers were able to group their lands in a way which allowed their conversion to a series of long, narrow fields. At Great Kelk, also in Yorkshire, the enclosed strips which George Grimston bought in 1719 can still be identified among the rectangular fields into which the remainder of the open fields were divided at the Parliamentary enclosure of 1849(16).

Enclosures of strips consolidated by agreements and sales tended to leave awkwardly placed and isolated holdings. As the process continued, therefore, it was sometimes found more convenient to divide the areas to be enclosed into fields of the shape and size required, without regard to the boundaries of existing strips. Such enclosures could be most easily and acceptably planned by a surveyor, and in the seventeenth century the use of such professionals increased in Yorkshire and possibly elsewhere(17). This development produced regular and rectangular fields of the pattern later created by the awards of the Parliamentary enclosure commissioners, and so provides a link between the earlier and the later methods of enclosure.

The final stage came in the late eighteenth and early nineteenth centuries. The background was the combination of a rapid increase of population and so of the demand for food, and the gradual end of the ancient waste as a source of new fields, for by the end of this period relatively little forest, marsh or moor worth reclaiming remained, and any substantial increase in production could only come from existing farmland. The immediate cause was the general introduction of certain innovations already established on advanced farms, notably a new implement, the drill, and new root, grass and clover foddercrops. The drill sowed seeds in rows that allowed hoeing between them, thus making it possible to control weeds on land that carried a crop and so ended the necessity of the wasteful fallow, while the new crops greatly increased the number of livestock a farm could carry. Between them these new resources offered the arable farmer more productive rotations and the stock farmer greater scope for selective breeding, as well as larger and healthier flocks and herds. But the new rotations required radical changes in the open field cropping system, and selective breeding required a degree of control over the movement and mating of livestock which was incompatible with communal grazing. Open field farming was considerably more adaptable and progressive in both organization and methods than was once believed, but improvement was slow, the needs of the time pressing and the opportunities tempting. So the change came in the more drastic form of the comprehensive enclosure of open field land.

The purpose of the enclosure movement of George III's time, therefore, was the dissolution of the inherited open field system and its replacement by one which allowed greater, easier and quicker exploitation of the new possibilities. Its principal instruments were, legally, acts of Parliament which authorized the extinction of existing rights to ploughland and grazing and the re-allocation of the land into individually occupied farms and, physically, the hedges and walls which divided new farm from new farm and new field from new field. Typically, the fields of

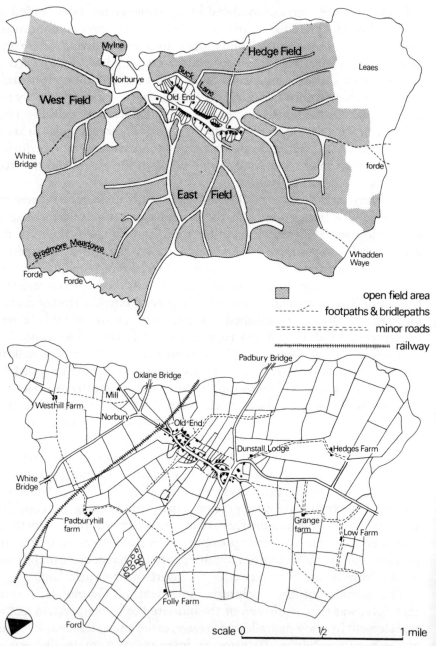

The effects of Hanoverian enclosure: above: the open field parish of Padbury in Buckinghamshire, from a map of 1591; below: the parish today, showing the field system and the outlying farmsteads built after the enclosure of 1796. (Based on Beresford, M.W. and Joseph, J.K.S., *Mediaeval England, An Aerial Survey*, 1958, pp.30, 33, 256–7). See photograph no. 15

the new landscape were larger and more regular than the older enclosed fields created by the efforts of individual peasants over the generations. The orderly, rectangular shapes, planned by the professional surveyors commissioned to administer the acts, continued the work of their privately employed predecessors. Indeed, these commissioners were the main architects of much of the modern agricultural landscape(18).

In areas of Parliamentary enclosure the change was rapid. John Clare published the first three volumes of the poems in which he so hauntingly described the older Northamptonshire countryside before he was 35 years of age. Even so, he wrote from memory, for as a youth he had helped to plant the lines of quickthorn which created the field system of the new landscape(19). The change was also extensive. Thus in Cambridgeshire, between 1796 and 1850, some 160,000 acres of open field and common pasture, nearly a third of the entire area of the county, were enclosed and replaced by new geometrically shaped fields(20). The result of this process was a substantial part of the field pattern we know to-day. To modern eyes such landscapes look as if they had been there all the time. Many enclosed fields, of course, are centuries old, but many are no older than the canals and factories of the Industrial Revolution(21).

A curious commentary on the speed and extent of Hanoverian enclosures in some counties came from foxhunters who feared that hedged or walled fields would make this sport impracticable and that the conversion of the commons to cultivated fields would destroy the fox coverts. In fact, the hedges made hunting more hazardous but added new thrills which appealed to sportsmen, while landowners preserved some old coverts and took to planting new ones. In Leicestershire, for example, the famous Botany Bay covert was planted in 1790, when the colony was in the news, and Grimstone Gorse by the Lord Cardigan who led the charge of the Light Brigade(22).

Only one example of a working open field system escaped the long process of enclosure. This is the famous parish of Laxton to which historians rightly make pilgrimage. Inevitably, this chance survival illustrates only one form of a highly varied system. But it provides an invaluable basis for the understanding of the principles and practice of a system which fed so many of our ancestors for so long(23). The open fields have also left a number of scattered traces which are among the most interesting relics of our rural past. In a few parishes, notably Braunton in Devon, some of the physical forms of open fields survive, though the strips are now farmed by individuals in the same way as any enclosed field(24). At Laugharne in Carmarthenshire, however, something of the old order still survives. Senior burgesses farm unfenced strips in the old communal fields and 'the strange anomaly and unique sight' of a combine harvester at work in a three-acre strip is followed by the ancient open field practice of communal grazing on the cleared land(25).

Elsewhere the boundaries of open fields are preserved in the landscape by relics of the hedges, walls or ditches which surround them, the pattern of strips by the hedges of the enclosed fields or by the line of streets which have replaced them. At Linton in Yorkshire, for example, the massive wall built with stones from the original clearance of the land in Saxon times still surrounds some 140 acres of former open field, which was enclosed into the present field pattern in 1793; the outlines of an open field engulfed by expanding Liverpool in the middle of the eighteenth century are preserved in part by the contemporary street plan north of the Exchange Station; at Batheaston in Somerset the edges of the old open fields are marked by garden boundaries, at Stanton in Shropshire by a line of trees, and at Hatfield in Hertfordshire by a path. Sometimes, too, the old boundaries tell a story otherwise forgotten. The parish boundary between Hampton Poyle and Islip in Oxfordshire follows the jagged line of the blocks of strips in the vanished open fields. So the fields predate the boundary, which shows that these villages were cultivating the land between them literally to the limit when they settled their frontier at some unknown date before the Norman Conquest(26).

But not all relics of the older order are immediately identifiable. Motorists from Duxford to Whittlesford in Cambridgeshire may notice some slight ridges in the tarmac. They are unlikely, however, to realize that these mark the site of headlands where peasants working the open fields turned their teams and dropped or scraped the mud from their ploughs and boots. This gradually accumulated into the slight ridges which are now 'fossilized for posterity' by the County Council Roads Department(27).

Ridge-and-Furrow

Sometimes the outlines of strip holdings or parts of strip holdings in the open fields survive in the form of ridge-and-furrow. These series of parallel ridges, anything from a few feet to several yards across and rising to two or three feet from the bottom of the furrow, still pattern many of our clayland fields. But the presence of these 'humpbacks' or 'stetches' does not necessarily mean that the site was once open field ploughland. It does not necessarily even mean that it was ploughland. For ridge-and-furrow is essentially a primitive system of drainage, although it was sometimes used for no very obvious reason on light soils where no artificial drainage was necessary. A series of minor 'ditches' were created by the mouldboard plough to carry the water off the field, thus keeping the ridges dry at the cost of leaving the furrows in constant danger of waterlogging. This system was generally used to drain ploughland, though also sometimes used in grassland(28).

The date of origin of this technique is uncertain, but it was known by Norman times(29). It was common practice in the Middle Ages and continued in general use until the development of cheap and effective means of deep drainage in the early nineteenth century. Although the strips of many open fields were drained by this method it was also used for other types of field(30). Ridge-and-furrow also survives in land which was never part of an open field system and from periods when the open fields were disappearing(31). Indeed, it lingered long after the development of deep drainage had made it obsolete. The ridge-and-furrow used to render marshes between the rivers Ore and Deben in Suffolk fit for arable cultivation, probably in the late nineteenth century, was perhaps an exceptional expedient for exceptional circumstances, but, surprisingly, one or two Suffolk farmers were still ploughing ridge-and-furrow in the years immediately after the Second World War(32).

Ridge-and furrow varies greatly in width with the type of soil, the slope and, above all, with local custom, and its measurements cannot be used on their own as a reliable method of dating(33). Sometimes, however, slight rises and kinks in ridge-and-furrow provide silent evidence of the consolidation of two end-to-end strips into one, the rises being the old headlands and the twists being made to connect ridges which were not quite in line(34). More obviously, certain forms of ridge-and-furrow record a major technical change, for although most ridges are as straight as the lie of the land allows, a number are curved in the form of an elongated and reversed S. These are relics of the work of the mediaeval ploughteams of eight oxen yoked in pairs. Such teams need a good deal of space in which to turn at the end of a straight furrow. This meant wasted or trampled headland, whereas only a narrow headland was required if the team ploughed a furrow which already partly turned them in the right direction. The S-curves, sometimes called aratral curves, thus produced all date from the Middle Ages, or possibly earlier, whereas straight ridge-and-furrow continued to be formed for another three centuries. This, it seems, reflects the better feeding of cattle or the importation of stronger, heavier cattle from Tudor times onwards which enabled ploughmen to use fewer oxen in their teams and therefore to turn in a smaller space. The resultant change was so comprehensive that by the reign of George III farmers had forgotten the origins of the S-curves and could not understand why their ancestors had created them. Some of these curved furrows have been fossilized into the field systems created by enclosures, where, for convenience, the new hedges and ditches followed the lines established by the old ploughteams(35).

Lynchets

S-curves preserve the memory of an historical technique. Lynchets, the cultivation terraces which form series of steps in the slopes of hills in many parts of the country, preserve the memory of historical land-hunger, for they are the result of the laborious contour ploughing of hillsides which would only be cultivated when all the more suitable land had been reclaimed. Some date from early times, but many are mediaeval, the highwater marks of the last attack on the waste by peasants striving to feed their steadily growing villages in the days before the Black Death. All have long since ceased to carry corncrops, but a number are visible some in grassy slopes, others, such as those cut in the Gog Magog hills near Cambridge by the ploughmen of Great Shelford, as obscure earthworks in woodland. But the needs which created and maintained them are best illustrated at Worth Matravers in Dorset, where mediaeval lynchets are carved into slopes so steep that when they were damaged by minor landslides they were reploughed and brought back into cultivation(36).

Commons and Greens

Most of the old communal grazings, the rough pastures and the village greens, have long been enclosed and incorporated into the field system. Some were enclosed by local agreement, some by act of Parliament in Hanoverian or Victorian times, some by squatters who illegally, but with local connivance, established their little farms on the only unoccupied land left in the area. The final stage in the long process of converting these communal pastures into individually occupied fields came in the late eighteenth and early nineteenth centuries, with the enclosure of most of the Mendips and Exmoor, of huge acreages of Southern chalk downland and Welsh commonland and many other minor survivals from the less exacting past. The 'most pleasing metamorphosis' of nearly 2,500 acres of upland waste in the Narber and Templeton area of Pembrokeshire into 'several large farms in a high state of cultivation interspersed with small portions of copse wood in a thriving state' was typical of the process(37).

The changes created new forms of landscape, but still left much of the older order which they only in part replaced. The contrast between the two is strikingly illustrated in the hills of Shropshire. Stoke St Milborough and Clee St Margaret are neighbouring parishes, but the commons of the former were enclosed, those of the latter were not, with the result that the enclosed and improved pastures of Stoke St Milborough run alongside the unimproved open commons of Clee St Margaret(38). Similarly, a few miles away, the fields of the fully reclaimed parish of Farlow border the heathland of Hopton Wafers with its scattered areas of farmland descended from old squatter settlements(39).

Sometimes the site of these old pasturages can be identified by the names or patterns of the fields into which they were divided. At Blaxhall in Suffolk, for example, are a group of fields called the Walks, such as First Ship (sheep) Walk, Second Ship Walk, Placketts Walk and West Walk. These mark the old common grazing or 'walking ground' for sheep, and the lack of old established hedgerow trees in this area suggests that the boundary of these Walk fields was formerly the boundary of the common(40). In Wales, where between 1795 and 1895 over a million acres of common land were enclosed, many of the fields created from it are 'immediately recognizable on the ground or on the map' by their size and shape(41). Indeed, the pattern of the fields into which the Town Hills and Burroughs Commons above Swansea were divided after enclosure in 1762 is still preserved by the roads of a housing estate built in the 1920s(42).

Sometimes the straightness of roads provides evidence of their former existence, because at enclosure-time it was easy for the ploughman to cut straight furrows across the open acres to mark the line of any new roads required. The Ely diocesan archives include a reference to payment for one man and two horses for one day 'to plough the road on the common' when Great and Little Wilbraham in Cambridgeshire were enclosed in 1797. At Battisford and Rockinghall in Suffolk roads called 'The Straight' still mark the lines of such work(43).

Sometimes placenames recall the greens and commons. In the Marches the names of new settlements created on enclosed communal pastures in the late eighteenth and early nineteenth centuries often included the name 'Green', hence Gisland Green in Cheshire, Prees Green in Shropshire and Walkers Green in Herefordshire(44). At Breighton, in the Vale of York, a lane still called the Outgang was once the track that led from the village to the long enclosed communal grazings on the uplands(45).

Sometimes the pinfold, the walled pound in which straying or illegally pastured stock were confined by the village official called the pinder, survives as evidence of the parochial control of the vanished grazing rights, notably and improbably on Hampstead Heath. In a less frequented part of the country, at Hope in Derbyshire, a pinfold was still used as recently as 1967, the pinder being allowed by a pleasing amendment of the ancient regulations to add to his charge for the release of the stock the cost of the phone call to the owners informing them that their animals had been impounded(46).

Various aspects of the enclosure of the commons have left their particular marks on the countryside. One is the legacy of the squatters

who, down the centuries, took advantage of the traditional belief that
they could not be dispossessed if they completed their cottage between
sunset and sunrise and so established their little farms on the commons
with the agreement or connivance of the local lord or village
community(47). The more ambitious, such as William White of Frampton
in Dorset who in the early nineteenth century raised himself 'by severe
self-denial and the most exhausting industry' from a day-labourer to a
120-acre farmer by reclaiming common heathland, worked boldly and on
a large scale(48). The majority were less obtrusive. The Victorian
squatters at Blaxhall, for example, either built a cottage on the common
or, more subtly, began with an improvised chicken run or pigsty,
converted it to a permanent structure if nobody objected and finally
hedged a small-holding and added a cottage(49). Most of these squatter
farms have now merged into the agricultural landscape, but a few remain
as islands of enclosed cultivation in otherwise open grazings(50).

Other byproducts of the enclosure of the commons include the small fields
created in some areas as allotments for the poor(51), and the long thin
fields which were originally greenways left as tracks to common grazings
or peatbeds and later enclosed(52). The curious evidence of gratton grass,
too, records the changing use of some of the ancient sheep-walks of the
chalk downs. Huge acreages of these were ploughed for corn in late
Hanoverian times, but abandoned to pasture again in the long
agricultural depression that began in the last decades of the nineteenth
century. The derelict ploughland, however, was colonized not by the
grasses which had formed the original closeknit and springy sward but by
the tall, wiry and coarse gratton grass. Many of these gratton grass areas
were ploughed once more during and after the Second World War, but
some remain on the downs near Eastbourne showing the site of the old
enclosures(53).

Relics of the greens or communal pastures around which villages
originally developed still survive in many villages and former villages
which are now parts of towns. Frequently, however, the greens have
vanished, generally under bricks and mortar, for when they were
enclosed, in many cases along with the open fields in Hanoverian times,
the land allotted to individuals was often used for building. Sometimes,
however, the memory of these greens is preserved by property
boundaries, as at Kingston in Cambridgeshire, where the green was
enclosed in 1815 and later built over, sometimes by the contrast between
the new buildings and the older ones which surround them. At
Thrandeston in Suffolk, for example, the outlines of the 50-acre green
which was enclosed in 1857 can be traced by the pre-nineteenth century
buildings standing along its former boundaries(54).

Many commons, however, survive. To most townsmen, indeed, they are the most familiar survivals of the older agricultural order. Those in the more heavily populated areas of the country now provide recreation for urban visitors rather than pasture for livestock, though some, such as Port Meadow, where the burgesses of Oxford graze their cattle and the unprivileged ride and walk, happily do both. In Hitchin, the Top Field, which has been used for games as long as anyone can remember, is still let subject to the grazing rights of the vanished Cow Commoners who are defined as the descendants of any inhabitant of the manor who occupied a cottage built before 1571. It is unlikely that these rights will ever be claimed, but in remoter areas the agricultural importance of grazing rights is still considerable. In particular, large areas of upland common in North Wales, some of which preserve an uncertain legal status from the days when Welsh custom governed their use, serve as an 'abiding reminder of an ancient agrarian economy'(55).

Less conspicuously, the practice of allocating annually among commoners the right to cut hay in parish meadows and later graze the cleared land, which formed part of a number of the older farming systems, has left occasional traces. The annual division between commoners of the Dole Meadow at Homersfield in Suffolk continued into the 1920s and some of the stakes which acted as the boundary-marks or 'doles' of the allotments survived to our own time(56). The more permanent stones which fixed such boundaries in some Pennine villages can still be seen, notably in the meadows between Cross Hills and Steeton, northwest of Keighley(57). Remnants of this communal system lingered in East Anglia into our own times. In the 1950s farmers at Bressingham were receiving payment for ceding their grazing rights to another farmer; in 1970 stock was still being pastured by owners of grazing rights on the common at Shelfanger. But the most remarkable institutional survival continues at Yarnton, near Oxford, where the commoners' right to cut hay and then pasture cattle on West Mead and Pixey Mead was allotted annually by literal ballot, using wooden balls each marked with one of the areas into which the land is divided. Recently the building of a main road through Pixey Mead has decreased the area subject to this custom, but the annual ballot preserves to this day the memory of an otherwise forgotten practice(58).

The Continuity of Change

It is convenient to consider change in field systems in terms of the main periods of change, notably the Tudor and Hanoverian enclosures. But change to meet changing agricultural demands has been a continuous process, although its rate and incidence differed in different periods and areas. Even the effect of enclosure was not always immediate. The date of a Parliamentary enclosure award may mark only the beginning of the local development of a new field system, for some farmers at first only enclosed the boundaries of their new holdings and provided internal hedges for their fields over the years at their convenience. Thus, Kilham-in-the-Wolds in Yorkshire was enclosed between 1771 and 1773, but 40 years later some of the farms created at that time still lacked internal divisions. There must have been many parishes like Ab Kettleby in Leicestershire where a print of 1824 shows huntsmen galloping over the open areas of enclosed farms whose only hedges marked the limits of their land. Sometimes, too, the establishment of the boundary fence around the new holding was followed by the creation of large fields which were later divided into smaller ones. It often took decades for the full effects of enclosure to be realized(59).

Whatever the overall pattern, farmers have always altered the size of their fields to suit their needs, dividing large into small or amalgamating small into large. The process is ancient. Some of the small 'Celtic' fields were amalgamated in Roman times or earlier(60), while at Castellnack in Cornwall a large enclosure which probably dated from the Iron Age was subdivided by mediaeval farmers(61). Later, a number of fields formed by the Tudor sheepfarmers were of immense size, up to 600 acres, which created problems of shelter and the control of grazing. Many, therefore, were later subdivided to suit more intensive systems(62). At Buckworth in Huntingdonshire, for example, the 25 fields with an average size of some 80 acres recorded in 1680 had increased to 122 with an average size of 16 acres by 1839(63).

More recently, fields were enlarged for convenience of working in Victorian times. In the 1840s, for example, Wren Hoskyns 'cut and carved large, square, comely-looking fields out of unaccountably shaped rhomboids' on his Warwickshire farm, and in the next generation the coming of steam power for cultivation caused occasional increases in field size to allow sufficient space for the new tackle to work effectively(64). The total acreage replanned by Hoskyns and his successors was small and the agricultural depression which began in the 1880s ended such attempts at improvement. But Victorian changes in the field system are a useful reminder that the farming landscape, apparently so established, is necessarily provisional, a temporary stage in a continuing process of evolution. The farmers of our own time who bulldoze hedges to create fields of the shape and size required by modern machines and methods have a long tradition behind them.

Hedges

Historically, the hedge is a means of marking the boundaries of an estate, a farm or a field and of restricting the movement of animals, both to keep stock in and predators out. Any other functions it performs, such as the provision of shelter for animals, soil or wildlife, are no more than accidental byproducts of its main purposes(65). Technically, it is a simple and convenient means of meeting an obvious agricultural need and its characteristics illustrate its origins. It is living and growing, the equipment of a pre-industrial age developed by local skills from resources provided by local nature, in this case spiky bushes, usually planted but sometimes, as described in Chapter 1, formed from strips of vegetation left as boundaries when woodland was converted to fields.

The farmer has been using hedges for many centuries. Hedges were so common in South Wales at the end of the Middle Ages that fifteenth century leases from monasteries invariably stipulated that hedges and ditches should be kept in good repair(66). In the parish of Conington in Huntingdonshire 62% of modern hedges existed in 1595, in the parish of Earl's Colne in Essex half the hedges shown on a map of 1598 were still in existence in 1950(67).

Indeed, recent research has shown that the hedge has a considerably longer history than was once believed. One of the techniques used in this research is a method recently developed by botanists and historians of assessing the age of a hedge by the number of species of plants it contains. In very general terms, a hedge will contain in a 30-yard length one shrub species for every century of its life, so that in such a length a hedge of mediaeval origin may have an average of six or seven shrub species, a hedge planted by a Hanoverian encloser only two. The formula is not, of course, an immutable law, but it is a valuable guide when used with commonsense and local knowledge. The number of species in any hedge, of course, is limited to the trees and shrubs likely to grow on a particular soil and it is improbable that more than 12 will do so even if the hedge is over 1,200 years old. On poor soil relatively few species will flourish and the method is therefore less reliable. Further, elms spread by suckering and so may suppress other species, consequently hedges containing elms sometimes give a lower count than the age of the hedge justifies. Again, local practice may influence the composition of hedges. In some areas it was the custom to plant mixed hedges, while in the Midlands hawthorn, which produces a quick-growing and stock-proof hedge, was commonly chosen as a hedging plant by Hanoverian enclosers and in this area Parliamentary enclosure can often be recognized by the dominance of this species(68). Here, as elsewhere, careful interpretation of results is essential. But the findings of this important new technique, combined with evidence from documentary sources, have made it clear that a number of hedges date from Tudor, mediaeval, Saxon, and possibly even earlier times.

There are numerous examples of the use of this technique in local rural studies, but it has also proved useful in an urban setting. According to tradition, the Lancastrian army at the Battle of Barnet in 1471 lined the hedge which now runs along a public right of way across Old Fold Manor Golf Course. An investigation by the Hendon and District Archaeological Society established the median date of its planting as the late fourteenth century. Since such a hedge would have been well established by the time of the battle, it suggests that the tradition is correct. The same Society also studied a hedge which crosses Lyttleton Playing Fields in Hampstead Garden Suburb and seems from documentary evidence to have formed part of the boundary of the Bishop of London's deer-park, first mentioned in 1241. This hedge was found to date from the mid-thirteenth century which supports the conclusions drawn from the written evidence(69). In the years ahead such studies should add very considerably to our knowledge of rural history.

Hedges are inevitably connected with boundaries and it is likely that most of the oldest surviving hedges were planted or grew naturally on the earth banks created when ditches were dug to mark the limits of estates or farms. It is possible that some Cornish hedges, notably in the Penwith peninsula, which originated in this way, may date from the Bronze Age(70). It is more than probable that others date from the Saxon settlement, for the boundaries they mark have not changed since the division of the countryside was agreed by its new lords(71). Indeed, boundary hedges are inherently less likely to be removed than internal hedges, and the probability that the boundary hedge is the oldest hedge on the farm was strengthened by the Hanoverian practice, previously described, of hedging the perimeters of holdings created by enclosure before dividing the enclosed land into fields. The point is appreciated by ecologists who emphasize the particular importance of conserving boundary hedges because they commonly contain a richer variety of plant life than the more recent internal hedges(72).

To the farmer, the hedges he has inherited from tribesman, peasant or monk, Tudor businessman, Stuart yeoman or Hanoverian landlord, are primarily pieces of fixed agricultural equipment. To the casual visitor to the lowland countryside, they are among the most attractive and typical features of the landscape. To the naturalist, they are the homes of animals, birds, insects and plants. But to the historian they are a valuable guide to the farming past(73).

Stone Walls

The upland farmer, like his lowland cousin, has long used local resources to identify his boundaries and divide his fields. His material, however, was stone, not bushes, and the story of many of the walls with which he patterned the hills is simpler than that of the hedges, for they were often built when the land was first reclaimed and have changed little since then. Climate and soil have ensured that man continues to farm the high hills with livestock rather than with crops and machines and so there has seldom been any need to alter field systems.

Stone walls form part of some lowland systems of farming, but elsewhere they are the means whereby upland desolation was converted to sheep farm. They separate communal grazing areas as well as individual fields; they provide flocks with shelter and in some parts prevent them from straying over precipices or into gullies; and they include pounds where flocks are collected for shearing or for marketing and wide-mouthed funnels narrowing down to walled trackways through which they are driven from fell to farmstead.

Men began to build these walls when they began to farm the uplands. The oldest to survive are the Dartmoor 'reaves' which still mark Bronze Age boundaries(74) and, like many of their successors, were probably part of the process of clearance. When Benedict, son of Edric Siward, established his farm at Cholwich Town on the south-west slopes of Dartmoor in the early thirteenth century, he built the walls of his fields and the banks of the lane which still leads to the farmstead that stands on the site he chose with stones removed from his new land(75). Similarly, the monastic landowners and their successors, who converted much of the Lake District wilderness to sheep farm, built many of their walls with stones from the pastures they created. We can judge the effort required from the record of an early Victorian reclamation in Bowland Forest, Lancashire, where the clearance of a single field meant the removal of 921 one-horse cartloads of stones(76). But the old reclaimers often left walls far thicker than was necessary, while the occasional cairns of surplus stones, sometimes in fields, sometimes built into walls, are permanent witnesses to their labours(77).

Occasionally the wall-builders dated their work. Up on High Wool Howe on the North Yorkshire moors, they proudly engraved 'Allerston Inclosure 1794' on the exposed upright stone of a Bronze Age barrow(78). Unfortunately such direct evidence is rare, and the contrast in construction between the simple piling of early work and the more systematic building in Hanoverian and Victorian times which followed the specifications of the Enclosure Commissioners can give no more than general guidance(79). Stone walls can usually only be dated by written record, but sometimes the shape of the fields they enclose provides a general clue, for here as elsewhere irregular, piecemeal early enclosures commonly contrast with the rectangular patterns established by the Enclosure Commissioners of the late eighteenth and nineteenth centuries(80).

A good deal of early work survives. A wall built by the monks of Furness Abbey in 1284 to enclose some 1500 acres of moorland can still be seen crossing the fells at the west end of Eskdale, just below Scafell, while miles of thirteenth-century walling on Malham Moor, Yorkshire, demarcate the old grazing grounds of Fountains, Bolton and Salley Abbeys(81). Incidentally, the connection between Fountains Abbey and Malham Moor is preserved by the name of Fountains Fell(82). A later example of walling can be found at Langfield, where 360 acres of moor were enclosed in 1615 by walls which still stand(83). The contrast between early, irregularly walled enclosures, some dating from late monastic times or even earlier, and straight, eighteenth century walling can be seen around Middle House above Malham Tarn(84). Most upland walling, however, dates from Hanoverian and Victorian times when huge areas of moor and fell were enclosed under the authority of Act of Parliament.

The total length of these upland stone walls is immense – in the Peak District, for example, they average some three miles of wall per farm or 20 miles per square mile(85). These miles of walling on remote hills, sometimes out of sight of human habitation and seen only by the occasional shepherd or hiker, recall the staggering physical achievement of our ancestors. They also illustrate the geological diversity of our islands and the skill with which our forefathers exploited it. The millstone grit of northern England, the limestone of the Cotswolds, the slate slabs from the quarries of North Wales, the granite of Dartmoor, all are very different types of material, each requiring from the builder a particular type of choice and arrangement as he selected and fitted his footings, his heartings, his through stones and his capstones to ensure a wall as lasting as the material from which it is made. Little is known of the early wallers, but in the eighteenth and nineteenth centuries much of the work in the north was done by itinerant bands of craftsmen, who were often illiterate, like Joseph Lancaster who built walls at Lanthwaite Green in 1841 and signed his wage receipt with a cross. 'Yet these men have, in another way, written their signatures on the fells for all to see and admire'(86).

Barbed Wire

Barbed wire was an American invention which played a crucial part in the development of the West where there was little local material for fencing. It is not clear whether the first barbed wire used in this country was imported or whether it was manufactured here. But it apparently appeared in the 1870s and its spread was rapid, for it offered the farmer facing sudden agricultural depression a means of keeping his fields stockproof for less cost than the manual maintenance of hedges. By the early 1880s it was sufficiently common to cause complaints from foxhunters and, incidentally, add 'Ware wire' to the traditional cries of the hunting field. In 1893 an Act of Parliament empowered local authorities to regulate its use(87). By the end of the century, therefore, it had become part of the normal equipment of the countryside. Under British climatic conditions, however, it is unlikely that any examples of early barbed wire survive on farms(88).

The Two Countrysides

There are, therefore, many different types of field and field survival, frequently visible together, sometimes side by side, sometimes the older below the more recent. Above Gordale Beck, near Malham in Yorkshire, for instance, Iron Age fields were cut by mediaeval lynchets which have in turn been overlaid by nineteenth century stone-walled fields(89); in the Isle of Purbeck some still visible mediaeval strips 'carefully respect' the continuous hedgelines which mark the boundaries of Saxon estates(90); at Harrington in Northamptonshire open field ridge-and-furrow is dissected by a seventeenth century drainage ditch and surrounded by nineteenth century hedged fields(91); in the Shropshire parishes of Church Pulverbatch, Condover and Stapleton it is possible to identify fields reclaimed from woodland in mediaeval times, fields formed by the enclosure of open fields between 1450 and 1650 and fields formed by the enclosure of commons between 1750 and 1850(92); and there are numerous examples of open field ridge-and-furrow under the modern field pattern(93). Similar examples can be found during many country walks. Yet these surviving differences are only part of a more general and pervading difference between the two kinds of agricultural landscape of which they form part. This difference is not absolute, neither is it always obvious. But the distinction between 'the ancient countryside' and 'the planned countryside' is a basic characteristic of our rural landscape and it tells us much about its history(94).

The 'ancient landscape' of small, irregular fields won by individual, seasonal effort, of wandering lanes and casual areas of surviving woodland is the legacy of the peasant. The 'planned landscape' of large, rectangular fields laid out by the surveyor with theodolite, plane table and measuring chain, of straight roads and disciplined woods is the legacy of the landowners and farmers of Tudor, Stuart and Hanoverian times(95). Some areas, such as parts of Sussex which remain 'in essence the work of the Age of Clearing', belong overwhelmingly to one countryside, some, such as the formal farmlands of Northumberland, belong overwhelmingly to the other(96). But in many the two countrysides are mixed. Even in areas where at first sight the effects of the planned landscape appear comprehensive, relics of the old order survive. At Ingham in Lincolnshire for instance, enclosure under an Act of 1769 caused 'revolutionary changes' in the landscape but left a few 'fossil features', notably the small irregular fields of earlier enclosures and the winding road which ran between them, while the original boundary between one of the open fields and common grazing land continued as a boundary between new fields and is still visible as a curving hedge(97).

A few instances chosen at geographical random illustrate this common intermingling of the ancient and the planned countrysides. The mediaeval colonization of Morfe Forest in Shropshire left winding lanes and irregular fields – and, incidentally, the name of one of its pioneers, Robert atte Lee, which survives in Lee Farm, near Dallicot – while the enclosure of the remainder of the forest in 1812 left straight roads and regular fields(98). Something very similar happened at Gillingham Forest in Dorset, though here much of the forest which had survived mediaeval reclamation was disafforested in 1624 and converted to farmland in the following years(99). The same contrasts are found around Wasdale Head in the Lake District, where the lower settlements are mediaeval and the enclosure of the fells did not begin until the eighteenth century(100), though the large regular fields of Dash Farm on the northern fells, which was enclosed in 1660, provide an early example of the type of field that later became common(101). As it is in the uplands, so it is in such coastal innings as the Dengie Marshes, where the irregular shapes of early fields preserve the pattern of the creeks and rills of the old saltings but the later fields are more rectangular as well as larger(102). And by a pleasing chance, the same distinction between the results of individual and planned enclosure preserves at Wereham and Caldecote in the East Anglian Brecklands the outline of the last infield-outfield system in the country. The privately enclosed infields are divided into small irregular fields, the outfield enclosed under an act of Parliament into large regular fields(103).

There are indeed many views in this country like those from Stour Provost, Dorset, where the visitor can see together isolated farmsteads with the fields around them which the predecessors of the modern occupiers reclaimed from the wildwood, long curving fields which were once the ox-ploughed strips of open fields, the orderly rectangular fields formed in the late eighteenth and nineteenth centuries, and the cottages and tiny enclosures of squatters on waste roadside land(104). The chapters of the generations lie open for all to read.

3

Water Supplies and Irrigation Schemes

A reliable supply of water is a prerequisite of any farm, and the effect of this necessity on the siting of farming settlements is a commonplace of historical geography. The spring and the springline are among the clues to the origins of many farms(1).

In these islands, however, water sources are so plentiful that they have aroused little interest and references to the development of farm water systems are few. Exceptionally, local studies mention the installation of boreholes and pumps in mid-Victorian times, the gradual disappearance of field-ponds in a Cambridgeshire parish and the contrast between the traditional 'meres' of Derbyshire, made by digging around a spring, and the smaller, more circular ponds fed by surface water rather than springs which were common in that county by the early nineteenth century(2). But most settled communities took their water supplies for granted and the best descriptions of the digging of ponds, many of which have now vanished, and the sinking of wells come from accounts of upland reclamation in the eighteenth and early nineteenth centuries(3).

The coming of artificial supplies was slow and late. Hydraulic rams were mentioned in late Victorian times, but the first reference in an agricultural manual to the public watermains which allowed farm buildings to be sited independently of springs and streams occurs in 1908(4). As late as 1924 the Hendersons, when surveying the Oxfordshire farm they were to make famous, noted among its assets 'a fine spring of water which supplied every field'(5). Significantly, a survey early in the Second World War, which found that only just over a third of the farmsteads of England and Wales were served by a piped water-supply and a quarter depended on wells while the remainder relied on streams, roof water and, in some cases, on neighbours, was followed by the introduction of an official scheme offering grants towards the cost on installing farm water schemes(6).

The only source of water which has acquired substantial documentation is the dewpond of the chalk and limestone hills. This is best described as a rather ordinary sort of pond which man has chosen to afflict with a quite extraordinary sort of mythology, for dewponds are filled not by dew but by rain and there is no evidence of extreme antiquity. The first reference to them dates from 1743, although it is possible to argue from one doubtful case-study that they were known in Saxon times(7).

Water is essential for plants as well as for men and animals, but natural supplies of water in any area do not necessarily bear any relationship to the needs of the farmer's crops there. In particular, the grass on which, in the days before rootcrops, his livestock depended for summer grazing and winter forage needs a considerable supply of water and is peculiarly susceptible to drought. When circumstances allowed, therefore, he sought to provide some of his grassland with a sufficient and controllable supply of water from convenient rivers. The irrigation systems he developed were known as watermeadows – areas of grassland watered from a river by a series of channels and cuts which could be opened and closed at will so that the fields could be flooded or drained to whatever level and for whatever period was required. But the new technique brought more than a supply of water to the land it served. The value of the silt and the sewage from upstream settlements which the water carried with it and deposited in the fields was obvious. Less obvious but equally appreciated was the temperature of the water, which arrived from its natural reservoirs in the hills at a constant temperature above that of the soilwater in winter and therefore encouraged growth in the colder months(8).

Predictably, this technique of 'floating' meadows was first developed when increasing population was making necessary the expansion and improvement of farming, apparently appearing independently in Herefordshire and Dorset early in the seventeenth century. It soon established itself as a means of providing more reliably than any other contemporary system of fodder production an invaluable 'early bite' in the hungry spring, a heavy crop of hay, and autumn grazing until the time came for the 'drownings' or controlled winter floodings. It spread to Hampshire and then to the Midlands and eastern England, finally reaching the West Country, where developments included an eighteenth century scheme in Devon served from a canal and a nineteenth century one on remote Exmoor 'before which the red deer bow their antlered heads'.

The total area of watermeadow created all over the country was very considerable. In the 1790s it was reckoned that there were between 15,000 and 20,000 acres of watermeadow in Wiltshire alone, and in the 1850s that there were some 100,000 acres in the southern counties alone(9).

By mid-Victorian times, however, improved rotations were producing more plentiful supplies of fodder. In the next decades imported feedstuffs and fertilizers further decreased the relative importance of watermeadows in the farming economy and the twentieth century brought changes which gradually ended the system. Labour costs rose and could not be reduced by the mechanization of either the operation or its maintenance; dairy cows, which tend to eat only the better grasses, replaced the close-cropping sheep which controlled coarse growth, while the weight of the new stock damaged the soft sward as well as bridges and the edges of ditches; and, finally, a sympton as well as a cause of decline, young men no longer wished to enter the exacting and shrinking trade of 'drowners' and the traditional skills required for managing these complicated systems grew steadily scarcer. By the 1940s controlled drowning had generally been abandoned and only natural flooding continued. By the 1950s only a quarter of the 4,000 acres of watermeadow in the Hampshire section of the Avon Valley remained effective and in the following decades the system passed gradually into history. In Dorset, Hampshire and Wiltshire in 1978 only two schemes survived in regular operation and two others in occasional operation when grass elsewhere was short.

But thousands of acres of abandoned meadows with their ridges, channels and derelict sluices mainly in the chalkland valleys record the former importance of this system. Their remains, for example, are a conspicuous feature of the Frome and Piddle valleys and traces of a simpler form of watermeadow, probably dating from the seventeenth and eighteenth centuries, can still be seen in Cambridgeshire, notably at Swaffham Bulbeck. Perhaps, however, the end is not final, for agriculturalists are considering new labour-saving methods of using some of these meadows and conservationists the possibilities of converting others to nature reserves(10).

One spectacular irrigation scheme, however, survives. Between 1816 and 1839 the Duke of Portland changed the course of a length of the River Maun centred on the village of Clipstone, three miles north-west of Mansfield, so that it could serve by gravity a network of shutter-controlled carriers and stone-paved drains which created a linear agricultural oasis in the wastelands of the Nottinghamshire Sands. It was a remarkable feat of engineering which converted 300 acres of sandy sheepwalk to rich pasture and improved a still greater area. The scheme, although slightly affected by colliery subsidence, still fulfils its original purpose, and the staff who operate it are traditionally called 'the Duke's navigators' after the men who dug the new watercourse when their contemporaries, the 'inland navigators' or 'navvies', were building the canals(11).

Other enterprising landowners and farmers also took advantage of nearby watercourses to create irrigation schemes on their land. The most famous was built in the late eighteenth century by Robert Bakewell, the famous livestock breeder, at Dishley Grange Farm in Leicestershire. He enlarged a scheme established by his father until it served nearly half his acreage, also using the main channel for floating turnips from the fields to the farmstead and for carrying boats which took manure back to the fields. Traces of this scheme are still visible and it is probable that investigations in other areas would produce evidence of similar local improvements(12).

4

Sources of Fertility

In the past, the farmer relied for the maintenance and improvement of the fertility of his soil mainly on the byproducts of his farming system, straw from his cornfields and excreta from his stock, which were trodden into manure in the farmstead and then returned to the land. More recently he has made increasing use of purchased fertilizers. Neither manure nor fertilizer leaves any permanent trace on the farm and their historical importance can be judged only by the surviving evidence of their means of manufacture. The relics of the early development of the substantial and varied industry which produces fertilizer are a subject of their own and outside the agricultural branch of industrial archaeology. But, as will be shown in Chapter 9, many farmsteads bear witness to the importance their designers gave to the accumulation and conservation of manure.

The buildings on some Dartmoor farms include ash-houses, where ash from domestic fires was stored for use as potash fertilizer(1). The main historical evidence of our ancestors' constant search for sources of fertility beyond those provided by crops and stock, however, is found not in the farmstead but in the landscape. The vertical groove, 15 feet deep in the top of the perpendicular chalk cliff of the South Foreland, near Dover, recalls the labours of generations of farmers who gathered seaweed on the beach and hauled it in bundles up the cliff on a rope pulled by a horse over a hundred feet above them(2). But this relic is exceptional, perhaps unique. The most common memorials of past preoccupation with fertility are found in the fields where farmers dug chalk or marl and burnt limestone.

Chalk and lime control soil-acidity and therefore improve the fertility of sour land. The value and function of marl, a generic term for a variety of mixtures of chalk and clay, are summarized in the old proverb,

> He that marls sand
> May buy the land,
> He that marls moss
> Shall have no loss.
> He that marls clay
> Throws all away.

On lime-deficient sandy land and on sour, peaty moss, marl improves the texture of the soil as well as correcting acidity. It also increases the water-holding capacity of sandy land. But adding clay to clay brings no benefit and marling clayland is an expensive way of adding any lime that may be required(3).

The digging and spreading of marl or chalk was known in Roman and mediaeval times – Nicholas the stargazing clerk in *The Miller's Tale* fell into a marlpit – and was widely practised in the eighteenth and early nineteenth centuries. For example, the numerous Kentish deneholes from which immense quantities of material were dug are now recognized as marlpits; in Cheshire marlpits were so common that the word 'pit' was used locally to describe any small sheet of water; and in some parts of East Anglia and in the Yorkshire wolds evidence suggests that there must have been a marlpit in nearly every field(4).

Marling was generally abandoned by the middle of the nineteenth century, and replaced either by liming, made possible by improved methods of transporting this bulky material from distant workings, or by the new purchased fertilizers, although chalk digging continued in Hertfordshire and some other areas until the First World War. The value of these longterm improvements to the soil is illustrated by the case-study of Applesham Farm in the Adur valley in Sussex, where the tenant in Napolenonic times applied one and a half tons of chalk per acre to his 150-acre farm annually for 20 years. Recent soil analyses show that the beneficial effects of the liming was still apparent(5).

Many of the pits thus created have since been levelled, but a number remain to record the early efforts of farmers to increase the fertility of their fields. It is, however, sometimes difficult to distinguish marlpits and chalkpits from old claypits or other workings and usually impossible to date them without documentary evidence(6).

From the late sixteenth century onwards farmers also burnt local or imported limestone to reduce it to spreadable powder(7). At first they burnt it in the open, sometimes in primitive 'sow-kilns', laying the stone on a bed of wood and then covering it with turf and leaving a flue, a practice which survived into the nineteenth century and has left traces in parts of Northumberland(8). Later, small permanent kilns were built which in some districts became common features of the landscape(9). The effective reclamation of many acid upland areas would have been impossible without the lime from such kilns and in South Wales, where visitors in late Hanoverian times noted that every farm had its limekiln, lime was the agent of a minor agricultural revolution which resulted in more productive ploughland and richer pastures(10). From the late eighteenth century, however, the largescale commercial production and distribution of lime gradually replaced the output of farm kilns which by the early twentieth century had become picturesque ruins, crumbling memorials of a vanished farm enterprise whose memory is also preserved in the occasional Limekiln Field(11).

5

Field Drainage

Drainage was one of the primary tasks of those who reclaimed farmland from the ancient waste. But over much of the country the water content of the soil remains a major limiting factor to the yield of crops. Excessive water harms soil structure and hinders the development of root systems, thus checking the growth of crops. It also delays cultivation and planting, since, in the words of an old agricultural proverb, 'wet land is late land', slow to warm up in spring and unable to carry implements until it has dried. In addition, wet land is liable to be damaged by the hooves of grazing cattle, while damp conditions encourage the pests that cause 'husk' in cattle and 'fluke' in sheep. It has been estimated that about half our modern farmland requires artificial drainage for full production. Field drainage, therefore, has been one of the continuing preoccupations of the farmer and it has left many relics in field and museum(1).

Ditch and Furrow
The ditch is the simplest form of field drainage. A plough-furrow which takes advantage of the lie of the land to carry water from a field to a ditch is its simplest extension, and from early times farmers on soils with poor natural drainage have sited their fields so that they could plough up and down the slope and the water could flow easily away. Any visitor to the open fields at Laxton, for example, will appreciate the skill with which the pioneers planned their strips to allow the furrows to discharge surplus water onto the unploughed areas of lowlying grassland among the arable fields(2). A further extension of this basic means of drainage is the formation in the field of a series of minor 'ditches' by ploughing the soil into hump-backs which keep the ridges dry at the cost of leaving the furrows in constant danger of waterlogging. This produces the familiar pattern of ridge-and-furrow described in Chapter 2.

Early Deep Drainage

Ditch and furrow provide surface drainage. Deep drainage, formerly also called hollow drainage, thorough drainage or under-drainage, involves the creation of underground channels through which water can run to ditch or stream. It is one of the most important forms of agricultural technology and has produced a substantial technical literature. But the immense investment of resources in this means of improvement which began in Stuart times, reached its climax between 1840 and 1880, and ended suddenly with the coming of the depression, has left few relics above ground.

Early types of deep drain made use of local materials which were laid in trenches to form channels through which water could pass and were then covered with soil. All were rendered obsolete by the coming of the mass-produced tilepipe in the middle of the nineteenth century, but some have left traces in the countryside.

Bush drains, which used hedge clippings or faggots, were known in the seventeenth century but may have been used earlier. This system was common in the late eighteenth century and, since it was simple, effective and required only materials that were readily available on most farms it survived in some areas as an alternative to the more expensive tilepipes well into the present century. In the 1920s the Ministry of Agriculture still recommended this method and some Suffolk farmers practised it into the 1950s(3). The life of these drains, however, was generally reckoned at 10 to 15 years, so it is unlikely that any are still working(4). A version of this type of drain using ropes of twisted straw has apparently perished without trace.

Stone drains were formed of stones either thrown at random into trenches or built into simple drystone culverts in the bottom of the trench. Like bush drains, they were known in Stuart times and were widely used in the late eighteenth century. Unlike bush drains they succumbed quickly to the competition of the tilepipe and by the 1870s were only laid in areas where the transport of pipes was impossible(5). A few stone drains, however, were found to be working or capable of restoration during the revival of deep drainage during and after the Second World War and some continued at least partially operational into the 1970s(6). Another traditional type of drain was the turf or sod drain made of turves laid in the bottom of a trench, sometimes over a narrow channel. In Yorkshire, in the 1960s, such drains were still being laid exactly as described in 1794 by the Board of Agriculture Surveyor in his report on the North Riding. In the same decade the remains of some were distinguishable in the Midlands. Many of these were still working 'after a useful life of over a hundred years', but they were nearing their end and were being replaced by modern schemes(7).

Tilepipe Drainage

The value of all these systems of surface and deep drainage was limited. In waterlogged areas, ditches sufficient for proper drainage would have required excessive space and created impracticably small enclosures; ridge-and-furrow kept only part of the land dry; and the organic materials used in the primitive deep drains decayed, while the stones tended to choke with silt. The more demanding system of farming created by the Agricultural Revolution of George III's time required some cheap and longlasting type of buried culvert that would carry water away from field to ditch. The need produced the tilepipe which became a means of major agricultural improvement. Indeed, in a sense, the tilepipe drainers continued in new form the work of the reclaimers who were by this time reaching the end of their task, for most of the ancient waste had been brought into cultivation. The axe reclaimed in area by creating new fields, the tilepipe reclaimed in depth by making available to crops soil resources hitherto denied them by excess water.

The tilepipe derives its curious name from the semi-circular or crescent shape, similar to that of the familiar ridge tile, of the early tiles used to form underground culverts. Drains of such tiles were first laid in the late eighteenth century. The early nineteenth century saw the local development and use of a variety of such tiles, then generally called horseshoe tiles, which were sometimes laid direct on the soil at the bottom of the trench, sometimes on a flat tile known as a sole. For a generation they were all handmade, but by the 1840s various forms of tilemaking machine were extruding different sorts of tile, including a horseshoe combined with a sole in the prefabricated unit. A variation occasionally used was the hollowed draining brick, sometimes, like horseshoe tiles, laid together face to face to form a pipe.

The ancestors of the modern cylindrical tilepipes appeared at the end of the eighteenth century. But such pipes were not widely used until their manufacture was mechanized and cheap mass-produced, extruded pipes replaced those made individually by wrapping clay around a mandril. The significant date in this change was 1845, when Thomas Scragg was awarded the prize offered by the Royal Agricultural Society of England for the best machine for making cylindrical tilepipes. The new pipes performed well and won such rapid acceptance that by 1870 they had in large measure superseded the tile and sole(8).

The agricultural depression which began in the 1880s virtually ended investment in deep drainage. It also caused the ultimate failure of most

19   The effects of piecemeal reclamation by settlers working outwards from their villages, which lie beyond the left and right of this photograph of Titterstone Clee in Shropshire. On the right, settlers from Farlow have created continuous fields, except for occasional areas of woodland and heath, up to their parish boundary, the hedge which runs diagonally to the crest of the hills. On the left, settlers from Hopton Wafers have reclaimed only small islands of cultivated land. Presumably the men of Farlow were more numerous or more energetic. In the middle of the photograph, the parish boundary turns from the straight line to include the fields near the camera, which suggests that the men of Farlow had won this land before the boundary was fixed.

20 Straight roads sometimes provide evidence of former commons, since at enclosure-time it was easy for a ploughman to mark the line of the new road by a straight furrow across the empty acres. An example from Swallow in Lincolnshire, enclosed in 1806.

21 The curving hedge in the centre of the picture marks the boundary between the parishes of Cadbury and Stockleigh Pomeroy in Devon. It originally marked the boundary of the estate of a Saxon called Cada and probably dates from the earliest days of the English settlement in this area in the seventh century.

22   Drystone walls at Chelmorton in Derbyshire, which stands 1,250 feet above sea level. The original settlers built their farmsteads along a stream, which is now piped, and created the long narrow arable fields which stretch up the slopes. The larger fields nearer the camera and in the background were the village grazing lands around the ploughed area. They were enclosed in 1809.

23　The 'ancient landscape' of small, irregular fields created piecemeal by
the efforts of generations of peasants from Saxon times onwards, each man
carving out his individual farm from woodland and scrub. The countryside
of South Devon.

24　The 'planned landscape' of large rectangular fields created by the
landlords of Tudor, Stuart and Hanoverian times. This area of chalk
downland was probably reclaimed for arable cultivation in the time of
George III. Cattle were wintered in the remote barn-and-yard to tread straw
into manure for the surrounding ploughlands.

25　Water meadows, which could be irrigated at will from nearby rivers by
systems of sluices and channels and could thus produce a good crop of
grass in dry seasons, were first made in the early seventeenth century. This
photograph shows a 'drowner', the highly skilled worker who controlled the
flow and level of the water, at work near Salisbury in the 1930s.

26 Abandoned watermeadows along
the Wiltshire Avon, showing the
irrigation channels.

27 The limitations of drainage by
ridge-and-furrow. A clay field in a wet
winter in Oxfordshire. The unridged
field in the background has probably
been drained with tile pipes.

28   Early nineteenth century drainage tiles, showing their evolution from the simple horseshoe via the horseshoe on a sole to the cylindrical pipe. A modern tilepipe stands in the centre.

29   From 1784 to 1850 there was a tax on tiles, but an Act of 1826 exempted tiles used for land drainage provided that they were marked 'Drain'. The horseshoe tile in the middle stood on the flat sole in the man's right hand. The top tile came from an estate brickyard which recorded its annual output.

30 Most Victorian deep drainage schemes perished from lack of maintenance in the long agricultural depression. But some survived or were reconditioned in the agricultural revival which began in the Second World War. This outlet, dated 1864, still forms part of a working scheme.

31 A demonstration at a farm park where breeds of livestock threatened with extinction are preserved. The animals shown are, reading from left to right, a Jacob's sheep, Longhorn cattle and a Tamworth pig.

32   Jonas Webb, a famous early Victorian breeder of Southdown sheep, who was one of the few farmers to be honoured with a statue, now in Cambridge.

33   A casualty of agricultural change. The agile, long-legged Norfolk Horn sheep were admirably suited to foraging on the bleak heathlands of their native county. But they were replaced by more amenable, more productive breeds when the heaths were enclosed and farmed more intensively. The last pure-bred Norfolk Horn ram died in 1973, and two specimens are preserved in the Norwich Castle Museum.

existing deep drainage schemes, for when the silt in neglected ditches mounted until it passed the level of their outfalls, the tilepipes, no longer cleansed by the flow of water they carried, gradually filled with soil. Like some even older stone drains, however, a number of nineteenth century installations were found in our own time to be still functioning or capable of rehabilitation(9).

Most of the installations of the Hanoverian and Victorian deep drainers, however, are literally dead and buried while, of course, such as survive show only their outfalls above ground. But many old tilepipes have been unearthed by farmers and builders and a number are exhibited in museums. A few of these tilepipes were dated or stamped with a local or estate crest by the brickyards which manufactured them, but it is difficult to establish either date or provenance very exactly in the absence of such exceptional markings. For one thing, tilepipes are seldom standardized. Throughout the Hanoverian period they were made locally in a multitude of brickyards, often estate brickyards, and they vary immensely in design. For another, drainage practice was equally localized, and the rate of change from one type to another depended on the decisions of individual landowners, farmers and drainers. Further, there is little documentary evidence on field schemes, for most of the original maps have perished. Nevertheless, there are certain clues and probabilities which can help to establish approximate dating.

In general, horseshoe tiles and handmade pipes date from the late eighteenth or first half of the nineteenth century. In particular, tiles or pipes marked 'DRAIN' date from between 1826 and 1850, for a tax which was levied on all bricks and tiles between 1784 and 1850 was amended in 1826 to exempt tiles made 'for the sole purpose of draining marshy land' provided that they were thus marked 'in so plain and distinct a manner that the same may be easily and distinctly legible to any Officer of the Excise' (10). Pipes of one inch diameter, the smallest used, can also be dated within two or three decades for they provide an interesting relic of technical failure. They were produced in the belief that the small bore would increase the speed of the water flowing through them and so keep them clear. Unfortunately the engineers had underestimated the drag factor, which slowed the movement of the water and therefore increased the rate of accumulation of silt until the pipes choked. The period when these 'pencil pipes', were used, therefore, was short, from the 1840s when they were introduced to the 1870s when they were finally abandoned.

Historically, the tilepipe takes its place with the axe, the plough and the hedge among the major agents of change in the farming landscape. The area it drained is uncertain. Although contemporaries reckoned that by the 1870s some three million acres had been drained, a recent estimate, based on sales of tilepipes between 1840 and 1890, suggests that the figure might be as high as twelve million acres(11). Neither was all the work well done, for the deep drainers were learning their trade. But the general success of the new technique and the benefits it secured were sufficient to earn it improbable recognition in contemporary fiction. Mr Mellot in Charles Kingsley's *Two Years Ago* refers to 'well drained fields which ten years ago were poor clay pastures, fetlock deep in mire, six months of the year', while Mr Brooke in *Middlemarch* advised Sir Charles Chetham, another landowner, to give drainage tiles to his tenants, clearly regarding this as sensible investment. In another novel of the period, Charlotte M. Yonge's *Hopes and Fears*, a young squire compared the colour of his sweetheart's hair to that of ripening wheat in a nearby field, though he spoilt the effect by adding that he had harvested 'the best crop we have ever had from the land, a fair specimen of the effects of drainage'. She eventually preferred someone else, which is perhaps not surprising, but his was the most engaging tribute ever paid to the work of the deep-drainer.

Another type of deep drainage is mole drainage, which has been described as 'tilepipe drainage without tilepipes'. The only relics of the history of this technique are the equipment and machines used, which are described in Chapter 8.

6

Historical Crop Varieties

The farmer's crops are the means whereby he transmutes inorganic compounds in soil, water and air into the organic substances on which men and animals depend for food. They are therefore the most basic of all his resources. They are also the most perishable. Some crops have vanished from our farmlands as a result of technical or economic change without leaving any substantial evidence of their former incidence or importance. Old vineyards can sometimes be identified by traces of terraces on hillsides, but woad and saffron are remembered only by occasional fieldnames and placenames and an emblem in the coat-of-arms of Saffron Waldron(1). The individual plants of continuing crops decay rapidly and all that survives from the millenia of cultivation in the remoter past are occasional chance survivals of carbonized seeds or seed impressions in pottery, of straw in old thatch, and the probably unique album of 112 pressed grasses collected on the Woburn estate in 1816(2). Less obviously, varieties of plant are destroyed by agricultural change when the farmer replaces old with new and discards those he no longer needs.

The farmer has long been accustomed to choose the varieties of each type of crop that best suit his environment and purposes. Tudor and Stuart writers distinguished different varieties of various crops and several of the most famous cereal varieties grown in Victorian England were bred between 1780 and 1840 from single ears of corn selected and sown by observant countrymen. Such work was valuable, but it was inherently limited, for choice was restricted to the best that local nature could offer.

In principle, the hybridization of plants offered an obvious means of breaking the restrictions which nature imposed and remoulding the vegetable world nearer to the agriculturlist's ideal. Thomas Knight, in late Hanoverian times, was probably the first man to make systematic use of hybridization in plant-breeding and certainly the first on record to hybridize wheat in Britain. But the results of such work were unreliable. The new varieties could not be maintained, and showed a mysterious and uncontrollable tendency to revert to the characteristics of their ancestors.

The change came in the early twentieth century, when Mendel's findings, first received in Britain in 1900, equipped the scientist with a set of principles far more reliable than the perspicacity of even the most gifted individual. By 1907, Biffen, whose work on wheat demonstrated the validity of Mendel's principles and laid the foundations of this new branch of agricultural science, described the 'modern plant breeding methods' made possible by the new genetic knowledge. Five years later the foundation of the Plant Breeding Institute provided an institutional commentary on his words. Since then a steadily increasing supply of improved crop varieties has been one of the major facts of agricultural life(3).

The gain to the farmer and the consumer is great. So is the loss to the industrial archaeologist, for the work of the modern plant breeder and the speed of modern change have combined to destroy most of the plant varieties grown before our own time. Year by year new varieties are developed to give improved performance or meet new needs. Year by year the farmer and the seed-merchants who serve him discard the older varieties and use or stock only those which best meet their immediate commercial purposes(4). By 1950 none of the 85 varieties of wheat listed in an agricultural encyclopedia of 1856 remained in cultivation, and in more recent years the rate of change, and therefore the rate of loss of the older varieties, has increased(5). For example, Squareheads Master was once probably the best-known of all varieties of wheat. Developed in Victorian times, it was so widely used that in the 1940s the saying 'when in doubt, sow Squareheads Master' was quoted among agricultural proverbs. Thirty years later it was so scarce that makers of corn dollies who value its straw for their work found it difficult to obtain(6). So varieties known for generations, or even centuries, disappeared within a decade or two. It was nobody's business or interest to preserve them.

There is now, however, growing recognition of the importance of historical varieties of plant as reservoirs of the genetic raw material on which plantbreeders depend, and the International Board for Plant Genetic Resources has recently been established by the FAO to co-ordinate efforts to preserve endangered strains(7). It is likely, therefore, that the future will see better conservation of our vegetable past. At present, however, such few and limited stocks of seed as survive from the multitude of varieties which grew in our ancestors' fields are maintained by various plantbreeding centres which use them in their work of crop improvement(8). There is no 'Agricultural Plant Museum' open to the public where historical varieties of crop are grown or their seeds preserved.

7

Historical Breeds of Livestock

In the British Isles nature and history have combined to favour the feeder and breeder of livestock. Climate, soil and rainfall favour the grasses and thus the grazing beasts which convert them into meat and milk, wool and draught-power, while successive waves of invading settlers have introduced and established a rich variety of types and strains of farm animal. British farming has always been predominantly a livestock economy.

Some of the limited legacies of livestock history come from the world of the dead. There are the occasional relics of some outstanding animal, such as part of the skeleton of the famous bull 'Comet' which is preserved in Darlington Museum. He was one of the breeding triumphs of the Colling Brothers, who founded the modern Shorthorn, and he was sold in 1810 for the unprecedented price of one thousand guineas. Another example is the complete skeleton of the famous Clydesdale stallion, 'Baron of Buchlyvie', who fetched a record price of £9,500 in 1911, in Glasgow Museum. Then there are fragments of wool clothing and parchments with wool fibres embedded in them which provide evidence on the types of sheep they once covered(1). There are also bones from archaeological sites which tell us much about the diet as well as about the flocks and herds of our ancestors and, in addition, from the age at which they were slaughtered, about the systems of management of the period(2). But other evidence comes from the world of the living, as surviving representatives of historical breeds now graze quietly in paddock and field.

The livestock we see in the countryside to-day are the victors, the temporary and provisional victors, in a continuing competition between types, breeds and strains for the economic favour of the farmer. They are, literally, his creatures, which he has developed or imported, modified, selected or discarded as the needs of the farm require. Indeed, changes in the farmer's choice of livestock are a valuable source of information on more general agricultural changes.

Historically, however, the farmer's control of the attributes of his animal resources is a very recent development. From the forgotten age when men first domesticated animals to the time of the Hanoverians, farmers did little more than make the best use of such stock as they had inherited. They appreciated the good and bad points of their beasts. They knew and practised ways of securing better performance by management and feeding. From time to time ambitious and enterprising men tried to improve their beasts, either by selective mating or by importing new blood from other areas or other countries. But such efforts were exceptional and the results limited. Until the eighteenth century there was no general recognition of the possibility of using controlled mating as a systematic means of remoulding livestock to suit the changing requirements of the farm.

The revolution in stockbreeding was a major theme of the Agricultural Revolution of George III's time which followed the increasing demand for food created by the growth of population and the development of industrial towns. The farmer met these profitable needs partly by cultivating more land and partly by improving his methods, notably by making greater use of new or unfamiliar forage crops, the turnip, the swede and the mangold and various types of grass and clover. These enabled him not only to carry more stock but also to assess genetic possibilities hitherto concealed by the effects of poor feeding, and so provided the improver with greater resources and better information for his choice of sires and dams.

Many farmers already occupied individually managed holdings of enclosed fields which allowed them to grow crops and breed stock as they thought best. Many others in this period came to occupy such holdings when the enclosure movement freed them from the old open field restrictions on rotations and converted most of the surviving communal grazings, 'where anybody's son mated with nobody's daughter', into hedged or walled fields which gave them full control over breeding policy. So there is basic historical truth in the over-simplification of the older schoolbooks in which Townshend the Turnipgrower and Hodge the Hedger are followed by Bakewell the Breeder. Forage crops and enclosed fields made possible the work of the Hanoverian and Victorian breeders.

The first known individual breeder in Britain was Webster of Canley in Warwickshire, who developed his improved Longhorn cattle between 1730 and 1750. He was succeeded and eclipsed in the next generation by Bakewell, the greatest of all breeders, who died in 1795. Within another lifetime the stockfarmers of the new tradition had established selective breeding as a major means of agricultural improvement, created most of the breeds we know to-day and made this country the studfarm of the world. There are some two dozen international breeds of farm livestock whose merits are recognized in all five continents and three-quarters of these originated in the British Isles.

'In the whole course of natural history', wrote Richard Jefferies a century ago, 'there is nothing more astonishing than the way in which animals of English breeds have supplanted others in countries which may be said to practise civilised agriculture . . . . A series of maps which showed the progress of English animal life over the surface of the globe during the last hundred years would furnish much matter for reflection(3).' It was, indeed, a remarkable achievement, one of this country's greatest contributions to the world, and the tradition continues to this day(4). But the men responsible for it have left few memorials beyond the breeds they created. Exceptionally, however, one was remembered in stone. Jonas Webb, the famous breeder of Southdown sheep who, from 1841 to 1856, held a near-monopoly of ram prizes at the Royal Show was honoured with a statue, which stands outside the offices of the South Cambridgeshire District Council in Hills Road, Cambridge.

The prerequisite of the breeder's success was the readiness of the farmer to develop and use improved types of stock and, conversely, to abandon those which no longer suited his purposes so well. Such a tradition was established early – the improved Longhorn cattle which were among Bakewell's most striking triumphs were obsolescent within a generation of his death – and has continued ever since. One sign of its power is the fate of the breeds which were weighed in the balance and found wanting.

The most obvious example of change in the animal balance-of-power, of course, is the end of the horse as an agricultural prime mover, although here the sucessful rival was the machine. The effects of competition between breed and breed under differing economic pressures are less dramatic but equally decisive. The process was shown at its crudest by the discovery in the late nineteenth century of an old well near Salisbury containing the bones of many scores of horned sheep. The bones were apparently the result of some eighteenth century farmer's decision to slaughter his flock of Wiltshire Horn sheep which he wished to replace with a new breed because he could find no market for them, presumably because other farmers were following the same policy. Significantly, the Victorian farmer who found the bones wondered who could have kept so many rams for his flock and why he had thrown only rams' carcasses down the well. The change of breed had been so comprehensive that he did not realize that all the sheep of the breed formerly traditional in his area were horned(5). But few changes have been as drastic as this forgotten local episode.

Sometimes discarded breeds have lingered in obscurity in a few areas, even on a few farms. For example, the famous Cotswold sheep were once a major source of national wealth, but when mutton became more important than wool, they were gradually replaced by other breeds until by the early 1970s only four flocks containing less than 150 sheep survived(6). Sometimes such breeds were transmuted by crossing into new breeds. Thus, in mid-Victorian times, the Suffolk Dun, the best of all traditional dairy stock, was crossed by East Anglian farmers with the Norfolk, a beef beast, to produce the dual-purpose Red Poll(7). And sometimes, like the Cumberland or the Dorset Gold Tip pig in recent years, they passed quietly into extinction(8). Changes in the world of poultry have been even more comprehensive, for most of the popular breeds of a century ago are now almost extinct, replaced by those developed to meet modern needs(9). The picturesquely named Derbyshire Redcap, for example, was once common. To-day only a few survive.

Here as elsewhere, the new is commonly the enemy of the old and the increase in recent years in the speed and pressure of agricultural change has meant a corresponding increase in the list of threatened breeds. Indeed, a few years ago a livestock judge could well have repeated in his own terms the haunting lament of Sir Ranulph Crewe over the fate of the great families which had formerly dominated English history. It seemed all too probable that Longhorn and Gloucester cattle, Lincoln Longwool and Wiltshire Horn sheep, Berkshire and Tamworth pigs, as well as many others would go the way of Bohun and Mortimer, Mowbray and Plantagenet. Fortunately the danger was realized in time. In 1973 the Rare Breeds Survival Trust was founded to ensure the preservation of endangered domestic species in their agricultural homeland, sometimes on commercial farms, sometimes in farm parks. In certain cases their future is further secured by a semen bank, as an insurance against breeding failure.

There are, of course, precedents for such preservation. The most impressive and picturesque animal survivals in this country, the famous White Park cattle, have been protected in private grounds at Chillingham, Dynevor and Hamilton ever since the woodlands in which their wild ancestors roamed were enclosed in mediaeval times. We owe much to those who have guarded them down the centuries and, indeed, in our own time. For early in the Second World War a representative group of such cattle were shipped to the Bronx Zoo to preserve the line in case this country was devastated, and their descendants are now on the King Ranch in Texas(10).

Respect for the past, an appreciation of the variety such animals add to the present, and the desire to conserve them for the pleasure and interest of the future are now reinforced by more immediately agricultural considerations. For every breed is a living treasure-house of unique genetical resources which, once lost, can be replaced only by chance mutation and not by human act. For man cannot make genes; he can do no more than select from those which exist in living populations. So the preservation of threatened breeds ensures the survival of genes and gene combinations which may be invaluable to the farmers of the future, either directly for crossing or indirectly as material for research into animal evolution, domestication and selection. The attributes of our present livestock may be unsuitable in the years ahead and attributes of little importance now may then be required. We do not know the demands of the future and we should therefore preserve the biological inheritance on which depend the possibilities of genetic variation and flexibility to meet man's unforeseen needs.

The importance of systematic preservation is shown by comparing examples of losses and recoveries in recent years. Thus, the Lincolnshire Curly-coated pig, originally bred to provide fat meat for farmworkers for whose board and lodging employers were by local custom responsible, outlived its purpose and failed to find a disinterested protector. It is now extinct, the last survivor of the breed dying in 1972(11).

The Norfolk Horn sheep was hardly less unfortunate. This ancient breed of hardy, long-legged beast, wild, agile and slow-maturing, was evolved for foraging on the poor, bleak heathlands of its native county. But it was physically and economically unsuited to the enclosed and intensive system established by the Agricultural Revolution, which provided hedged fields of succulent rootcrops and grasses on which sheep could be confined by hurdles but which required in return rapid growth of mutton. Not even the acknowledged quality of its lean, sweet meat could save it from the competition of the more placid, more productive breeds which suited the new economy. By the middle of the nineteenth century Norfolk Horn flocks were rare, by the early twentieth century they were no more than local curiosities. Finally, from 1919 to 1954 one loyal farmer maintained the only surviving flock. After his death the handful of surviving sheep were lodged first at Whipsnade Zoo, then at the National Agricultural Centre at Stoneleigh in Warwickshire. But by this time they were too few to allow expansion without harmful inbreeding and the last purebred Norfolk Horn ram died in 1973. By crossing survivors with Suffolk sheep which include a Norfolk strain, however, a form of the old breed which preserves much of its genetic material has been created to continue a type of animal as near to the original as is now possible. Preserved examples of a Norfolk ram and ewe can be seen in Norwich Castle Museum to which they were presented nearly 50 years ago by their last breeder(12).

Gloucester cattle, however, provide an encouraging example of recovery before the point of no return is reached. This hardy, general-purpose breed, which produced good plough-oxen and excellent lean meat, is known mainly through its dairy qualities. Traditionally, it served the cheese industry of the valleys of its homeland and neighbouring counties and gave the famous Double-Gloucester cheese its name. The small fat-globules in the rich milk of this breed produced a fine, even-textured cheese but did not rise readily to the surface of the milk and so necessitated the double setting and skimming of the milk. But no major improver arose to develop its potentialities and in the days of the Agricultural Revolution it was gradually replaced by other breeds. As early as 1834 it was described as 'nearly extinct'. That it survived to our own time was due mainly to the efforts of successive Dukes of Beaufort who kept a herd of them and encouraged their tenants to do the same for the agreeably uneconomic reason that these placid animals were not frightened or scattered by the Beaufort hounds which from time to time ran through their pastures. Then, in 1973, the defunct breed society was recreated and in the following year Gloucester cattle returned to the ring of the Three Counties Show after an absence of 39 years. The number of these cattle is small and their prospects uncertain, but their revival illustrates the practicability of preserving types and strains of animal which, without care, would be irretrievably lost(13).

So the present generation is privileged. It is the first to be able to see many types of farm animal which once played an important part in agricultural history and have now been saved from extinction and preserved in farm parks(14).

8

Tools, Implements and Machines

Introduction

In the days of the village economy day-labourers were expected to come to the farm equipped for work. Any random group could probably muster between them 50 or 60 different types of tool. In the days of the factory system, the number of implements exhibited at the annual Royal Show by Victorian manufacturers ranged from 4,000 to over 10,000(1). Few men use more tools, implements and machines than the farmer. He uses them to form and maintain the fixed framework of his farm, to raise a variety of crops and livestock under a variety of physical conditions, and to undertake a variety of operations from cultivation and harvesting in the field to storage and processing in the farmstead. He has also harnessed to his needs a variety of forms of organic and inorganic power. Further, he has drawn on the technical legacies of many different periods so that, for example, types of handtool that were traditional in Tudor times continued in use alongside the products of Hanoverian improvers and Victorian engineers. In the 1970s an elderly Sussex farmer found that 20 types of tool listed in a 1750 inventory of a local farm could well have been used on the same farm when he was a boy(2) and the last oxteams were contemporary with the first tractors, the last scythes to cut corn with the first combine-harvesters.

Inevitably most of the working equipment of the past has perished, but it has produced a substantial literature and left a considerable and varied mass of material in the museums and collections with which this generation is so well served. These publications and exhibits between them give an invaluable introduction to many of the needs, resources and methods of our farming ancestors.

The Fixed Equipment of the Farm

Field Drainage Tools

The simplest forms of field drainage are the ditch, dug by hand with a spade, and the furrows of the ridge-and-furrow system, created by ploughing (See Chapter 2). Specialized spades for trenching were known in Stuart times and improved forms of spade were developed in the eighteenth century. But a comparison of nineteenth century and modern sets of drainer's tools suggests that once standardized, presumably during the establishment and expansion of tilepipe drainage in early Victorian times, they changed little, while the fork once used for pressing down brushwood in bushdrains, and now in the Norfolk Rural Life Museum, recalls the survival of older and simpler techniques(3).

In the late eighteenth and early nineteenth centuries the labour of cutting trenches or water-furrows was sometimes lightened by the use of horsedrawn drainage ploughs and in the early nineteenth century subsoil ploughs were developed to increase the permeability of the soil by breaking up the subsoil without bringing the sour, unworked earth to the surface(4). Another new and more effective form of drainage, too, required animal or mechanical power. This was mole draining, which forms undergound channels by dragging through the soil a metal bar with a blunt point appropriately called a mole.

Primitive manual forms of the mole drain principle, plug draining, were used in the seventeenth and eighteenth centuries. Sometimes a man standing in a trench or hole drove rods called plugs into the soil to form drains, sometimes a pole with a chain on the end was laid in a trench, the trench was filled and rammed, and the pole then hauled out, both processes being repeated until a length of underground drain was formed. But these laborious methods were rendered obsolete at the end of the eighteenth century by the development of the mole plough, an implement which combined a cutting edge and a mole(5).

Early mole ploughs were drawn by teams of up to 20 horses harnessed either directly to the plough or, since the power required was considerable, to the capstan which hauled it. Such capstans so economized on effort that some were worked by gangs of men or women. But the Victorian engineer changed all that. In the 1850s John Fowler adapted steamdriven equipment, originally designed to lay tilepipes, to the more successful haulage of mole ploughs and muscle-power was gradually replaced by steampower. A lifetime later the steam-engine was in its turn replaced by the tractor. But the old techniques survived long. Horse capstans, an example of which is preserved in the Museum of East Anglian Life, were still at work in the 1920s, steam sets 30 years later(6).

Indeed, the equipment of the steam age often outlived the power for which it was designed, for a number of nineteenth and early twentieth century mole ploughs hauled by crawler tractors 'in powerful and effective alliance of old and new' continued in use in the years after the Second World War and a few drain fields to this day(7).

Hedging Tools

The hedge has many agricultural virtues, but it has one serious weakness. It grows upwards, whereas the farmer wants it to grow sideways to create a stockproof barrier. Periodically, therefore, he has to 'lay' his hedges by cutting into a proportion of the main stems, bending them over and securing them with stakes and then interweaving stems and stakes with withies to form a living wall which is later reinforced by new growth. There are various regional differences in styles of hedge-laying but every hedger uses the same sort of tools. He needs an axe, a rake, a spade and a mattock for clearing, a mallet for driving stakes into the ground and a hedge knife or 'slasher'. His essential tool, however, is the billhook. Types of billhook vary with area, although the differences apparently reflect local tradition rather than different methods of cutting. The most common are the double-edged Leicestershire and Yorkshire pattern and the single-edged 'rodding hook' used on the Welsh borders(8).

The first mechanical hedgecutter appeared in 1931, when few farmers could afford to maintain their hedges. These machines control the spread of exuberant hedges cheaply and conveniently but do nothing to keep them stockproof(9).

Dry Stone Walling Tools

Like the hedger, the builder of mortarless stone walls uses a local, natural product and his manner of working varies from area to area. His tools, however, are more standardized. Some, such as the shovel or spade, the pick, the stone hammer and the pair of builder's lines, are used by other craftsmen. But the sign of his particular trade is the walling frame, of two boards fastened with crosspieces, which establishes the height of the wall and the slope of its sides in an outline to which the waller gives permanent shape(10).

Watermeadow Tools

The maintenance of watermeadows (Chapter 3) required specialized tools. Some of the spades and other implements used in the Avon Valley meadows, including a long sectional weedknife that was dragged in a zigzag motion up the river by two gangs of three men, one on each bank, are in the Breamore Countryside Museum, Hampshire.

Crop Production and Processing

Manure and Fertilizer Handling

The essential tools of traditional muck-handling were the familiar dungfork, sometimes reinforced by the dungspade or dungsaw to cut through matted, well-rotted manure, and the dungdrag to pull manure from the dungcart on to the field. A localized tool, the muck knocker, was used to spread cow pats on the Midland fattening pastures. It was similar to a hoe, but had a ring instead of a blade(11).

Horsedrawn mechanical muck-spreaders were introduced into Britain in 1905, but few were bought and it was not until the coming of the tractor that this major chore was mechanized(12). Various types of fertilizer drill were marketed in Victorian times, but this implement was not generally used until the twentieth century(13).

Ploughing

For over 15 centuries the modern form of plough, which breaks the soil with a share, loosens it further by making a vertical cut with a coulter and then raises and overturns it by sliding it over a mouldboard, has been the farmer's primary tool in the preparation of a seedbed. 'As I go, it is green on my one side and black on the other. What I tear with my teeth falls to my side.' So says the plough in a Saxon riddle, so says the plough behind a crawler-tractor(14). The surviving ploughs of our forefathers tell us much about the evolution of particular types of plough for particular circumstances, about the use of different materials, the application of scientific principles to their design and the replacement of the village craftsman-made tool by the factory-made one. But they are all variations of an accepted theme, recognizable descendants of their ancient prototype.

The older ploughs seen in our museums were essentially local products, made by local craftsmen according to local tradition to meet local needs, and they illustrate the immense variety of local types of plough which the county reporters of the Board of Agriculture described during the time of the Napoleonic wars. Significantly, they were generally named after their area of origin – the Hertfordshire plough, for example, which was eventually in general use, particularly in the Midlands, in the seventeenth and eighteenth centuries, the light Norfolk and Suffolk ploughs for sandy soils and the most longlived of them all, the Kentish plough, also called the turnwrest plough since it was fitted with moveable mouldboards which allowed all furrows to be turned one way. The Kentish plough, which was known in the seventeenth century but may have originated earlier, continued in general use in some parts of its native county until the First World War, and was occasionally used even later for ploughing and, finally, for destroying weeds(15).

The earliest forms of mouldboard ploughs were made of wood, except for the iron share and coulter, and the mouldboard was, literally, a board. But mouldboards plated with iron appeared in the early eighteenth century, notably on the Rotherham plough which was patented in 1730 and remained popular for a lifetime. Iron mouldboards came a generation later. The manufacture of the first wholly iron plough about 1770 was followed by half a century of detailed development and improvement, including the construction of ploughs of detachable and replaceable parts so that breakages no longer necessitated a visit to the blacksmith. In this period, too, the first modern ploughshare was made and patented by Robert Ransome in 1803. According to the legend he noticed that molten iron which had accidentally fallen on a cold stone floor formed a hard underside. So he began to manufacture cast-iron shares with the undersides chilled which sharpened themselves in use as the top wore away more quickly than the chilled iron below it, thus leaving the harder lower edge permanently protruding.

The appearance in 1843 of Ransome's 'Y.L.' plough marked the final stage in the transition from the wooden to the iron plough, although in parts of Sussex wooden mouldboards were used into early Victorian times and wooden ploughs with iron parts continued to be made into the present century. An example dating from 1919 is in the Welsh Folk Museum. The reason for such survivals was more than mere conservatism: wooden ploughs resisted the wear of flinty soils better than light iron ploughs and could be repaired cheaply and conveniently on the farm(16). But they represented a failing tradition, and the Y.L. plough illustrated a change in methods of production as well as in materials. For by now the centralized manufacture of ploughs in factories was replacing local manufacture by village carpenters and blacksmiths, and from this time onwards ploughs were increasingly known not by their areas of origin but by the names of the firms which manufactured them.

Nevertheless, apart from the development of multi-furrow ploughs for the steam-engines which began to challenge the horse-teams in the 1850s, this change in the method of production led to few changes in the character of the product. In the later nineteenth century there were various improvements in the plough but no fundamental alterations. In 1939 a Ransome's plough manufactured in 1839 was being used on a Hertfordshire farm and the Y.L. plough was still selling well(17).

The Breast Plough
This primitive and laborious implement derived its name from its blade,

not from the chest of the unfortunate man who pushed it through the soil. It was not a true plough but a spade with a long handle which was laboriously propelled by the operator's padded thighs. It was used for cutting turf or removing a layer of topsoil which was then burnt to destroy weeds and pests and returned to the land to improve the tilth. Long obsolete in agriculture, the breast plough survived in the market gardens of the Vale of Evesham until the end of the nineteenth century and on allotments in Suffolk and Gloucestershire into the 1930s. The example exhibited in the Science Museum was used in Gloucestershire until 1926 and a 'modern example' of such a plough was bought from a Gloucester ironmonger as late as 1936(18).

Cultivations

Ploughing is only the first stage in the preparation of a seedbed. Further cultivations are necessary before the land can be sown. Until the end of the Middle Ages much of the work of breaking down a soil to form a tilth was done by human arms and mallet-like wooden beetles or mauls. Rollers, drawn by horses or oxen, are mentioned in sixteenth century literature and by the end of the eighteenth century, when they finally superseded the beetle, a variety of locally made rollers of iron, wood and stone, including tree trunks with iron spikes driven into them or iron rings bound round them, were in use. Then, in the early nineteenth century, the factory system began to produce the iron rollers from which those on to-day's farms are descended, though wooden rollers continued in use in Hampshire and Dorset up to the 1930s, stone rollers in the West Country even later, while both types were 'not uncommon' in parts of Wales in the 1950s(19).

The history of the harrow, the other main implement traditionally used for preparing a tilth, is longer but similar in principle. It goes back via Tudor and mediaeval timber frames with iron spikes to primitive combinations of log and bush or hurdles interwoven with brushwood. But harrows, too, were remodelled in iron by the factories which from early Victorian times onwards produced a series of proprietary types which differed in construction rather than principle from their pre-decessors. Here again, however, the old forms survived. In some areas of Wales the *drainglwyd* or 'thorn gate' of hawthorn bushes tied to a gate or wooden frame was still at work in the 1930s, and the wooden harrow in the 1960s(20).

The new industrial order used its mastery of materials and methods to revolutionize old and develop new types of equipment and by early Victorian times a variety of proprietary iron implements with suitably aggressive names – grubber, clodcrusher and extirpator – were working

the soil and destroying weeds more effectively than the simpler products
of an earlier age. The story of the scarifier illustrates the general process.
Originally a Scottish implement, this timber frame with iron tines was
introduced in the early years of the nineteenth century to Suffolk where
the manufacturer, Arthur Biddell, marketed first an improved model in
the traditional materials, then a model in cast-iron and finally one in
wrought iron. A wooden harrow with iron tines which appears to be an
early example of a Biddell scarifier can be seen at the Museum of East
Anglian Life. By the time of the Great Exhibition in 1851 the farmer was
equipped with a range of still familiar iron implements which was
completed by the addition of the springtine harrow and the diskharrow,
the latter an interesting early example of American technical influence, at
the turn of the century. The Victorian engineer left the farmer a valuable
legacy. Some of his implements were still in use in the 1950s(21).

Sowing

'Behold, a sower went forth to sow.' Sowing remained a manual job on a
few farms into this century, and lingered in Cumbria into the 1950s and in
parts of Wales into the 1970s(22). So there are still a few people who can
remember the measured tread of the broadcasting sower as he rhythmically
cast the seed to right and left. Many examples of the hopper and seedlips
in which he carried the seed survive. So, too, do dibbling-sticks for the
handplanting of seeds with which Hanoverian farmers ensured the
regular spacing of corn and reduced rural unemployment by the extensive
use of cheap labour. Seed fiddles, operated by a disk turned by a bow, and
used for the sowing of small seeds are still found in occasional use(23).

The mechanization of sowing began with the invention of the modern
drill by Jethro Tull, who produced his first model about 1700. This was a
horsedrawn machine, consisting of boxes containing seed fixed into a
wheeled framework, which sowed seeds in 'drills' or rows. The seeds were
scooped out of the boxes by cavities in a roller which was turned by the
wheels as the drill moved forward and dropped through a tube into lines
in the soil which were cut by coulters.

The use of the drill spread slowly and did not become general practice
until the early nineteenth century. By this time a number of drills and drill
ploughs for sowing cereals and other seeds had appeared on the market
and a variety of improvements in detail had been introduced into the
design. The most important of these innovations was a system of small
cups to feed the seeds into the tubes through which it reached the soil,
which was patented by James Cooke in 1782 and soon became popular.
But there was no fundamental change in the original principle and the
early Victorian type of seed drill, which was essentially a developed and

factory-made version of Tull's invention, has remained in use with only minor modifications to our own day. A drill dating from the 1830s, which is now in the Museum of Rural Life in East Anglia, was still sowing seeds in 1964, and a drill of about 1850 in the Agricultural Museum of Wye College is described in the 1975 Guide as 'not substantially different from machines made today'. Jethro Tull had done his work well; his drill achieved the first advance in the mechanization of field work since animal-power was harnessed to the plough and later generations have done no more than give improved form to his original idea(24).

Weeding the Growing Crop

Traditionally the farmer relied on hand labour, with such hand tools as weedtongs, weedhooks and thistlegrubbers, to control the weeds which competed with his crops. The eighteenth century brought the horsehoe which so literally followed Tull's new drill and worked between the rows of plants it had sown, thus giving the farmer a far quicker and less laborious way of controlling weeds on land that carried a crop. One of these implements should stand alongside every drill exhibited in museums, for it continued the technical revolution which the drill began. It is significant that Tull called the book he published in 1731 not *The Drill* but *Horsehoeing Husbandry*. Here, too, the Victorians brought improvement by developing the horse steerage hoe which enabled the operator to control the wobble caused by the irregular movement of the horse and so keep a straight course between the rows of plants(25).

Nevertheless, the old ways continued, for handweeding, however slow and exacting, is potentially more thorough than weeding by horsehoe and consequently hand tools of mediaeval type survived into the age of the chemical spray. 'Weeding irons' were used in north Devon cornfields until the Second World War and old weedhooks, very similar to those shown in the Luttrell Psalter were found in a Suffolk village in the 1950s, although in recent years they had been used not for weeding but for blackberrying(26).

Harvesting and Stacking the Corn Crop

In pre-mechanical times, corn was cut by scythe or sickle, the latter often in conjunction with the bagging hook which held the stalks conveniently for the harvester, and both lingered long after the coming of mechanical harvesting. The sickle was used in some areas until at least 1900 and exceptionally into the 1930s(27). Until the First World War harvest workers were expected to be proficient with the scythe to clear roadways round the cornfield for the reaper, cut laid crops and replace the machine when it broke down(28). Scythes were used for cutting corn in parts of

Wales in the 1930s and occasionally for badly laid crops as late as 1948. They are still found on some fell farms, but are there used for cutting bracken, not corn(29).

Cutting implies sharpening. Consequently, 'strickles' or 'ripe sticks', pieces of wood greased and covered with sand and, later, 'sharpening stones', were essential items of the reaper's equipment. So, frequently, were gloves worn for protection against the thistles which grew in a profusion forgotten since the introduction of weedicide sprays. The cut corn was bound into sheaves with ropes woven from straw, stooked in the field to dry and finally carted to ricks which were later thatched.

Various early inventors tried to develop horsedrawn reapers, mostly with some form of mechanical sickle or scythe. The first successful mechanical reaper was invented in 1826 by Patrick Bell, who used the new principle of the cutter bar. His horsedrawn reaper carried two sets of sharp triangular blades on two bars. The lower bar did not move, but the upper bar was given a reciprocating movement by the wheel of the machine and so cut the corn by a kind of scissors action, which is the system used in all subsequent reapers. His reaper was little used, mainly because of manufacturing difficulties. But shortly after Bell had produced his machine, Cyrus McCormick, an American farmer-inventor, developed a very similar reaper, although his was pulled by horses, whereas Bell's machine was pushed. McCormick showed his reaper at the Great Exhibition of 1851 in London, as did Hussey, another American inventor, and the rivalry between them gave considerable publicity to both. The possibilities of the new technique were immediately realized by British manufacturers, ten of whom exhibited their reapers at the Royal Show of 1852, 45 in 1863.

The first major improvement on the original design was introduced in 1862, when the laborious manual work of raking the cut corn off the binder's platform was mechanized by the side-delivery apparatus of the 'sail reaper', so-called from its arms which revolved like those of a windmill. This laid the corn at intervals along the ground where it could conveniently be tied into sheaves. The second improvement followed in 1878. This was the mechanical knotter which tied the cut corn into sheaves, thereby freeing human fingers from one of the most exacting of all farm operations and converting the reaper into the reaper-and-binder. By the 1880s the design of this machine was stabilized and it continued with little change until it was rendered obsolete a quarter of a century ago by the coming of the combine-harvester. It was, however, typical of the varying rate of technical change that a reaper requiring manual tying was still in use on a farm in Yorkshire in the 1920s, the decade in which the 'combine' was introduced into Britain(30).

The reaper-and-binder, however, only mechanized part of the harvest routine. The farmer continued to part-dry his corn in the wigwam 'stooks' of piled sheaves which are now a fading memory. The sheaves were lifted on to a waggon and then stacked, either in a building or a rick. Sometimes the ricks stood on frames supported by mushroom-shaped stones to prevent vermin reaching them. Originally, these mushrooms were made of local stone, but in the early nineteenth century prefabricated cast iron frames and supports were produced commercially. Examples of Victorian frames which continued in service into the 1940s are at the Museum of East Anglian Life. Various forms of horsedriven elevator were marketed in the late nineteenth century, but on most farms, as some of the older generation will remember from aching experience, stacking continued to the end as a manual operation(31).

Thrashing

The corn harvest traditionally ended with noisy celebration as tired men bore from the field with uncomprehending ritual the mysterious last sheaf in which their ancestors had seen the dwelling place of the spirit of the corn, taking refuge like a frightened rabbit in the last standing stalks. This was followed by a feast in the barn. Such harvest rituals as the preservation of the last sheaf and its connection with corn dollies are primarily the concern of the anthropologist, but the industrial archaeologist may be able to contribute evidence on the reasons for the end of this ancient custom. In the 1920s a farmer, who remembered it from his youth but found no contemporary survival, felt that the reaper-and-binder was at least partly responsible for the change(32). Another custom which might have survived the reaper-and-binder but could not have survived the combine-harvester, was the ceremonial placing of a green bough on top of the last waggon-load of corn.

In the months after harvest, however, the barn changed from a place of feasting to a place of dreary labour. The straw ropes around the sheaves had hardened in storage, and were cut by a special knife with a sharply turned blade and the corn spread on the thrashing floor of the barn, where the flailers separated the grain from the straw and chaff. Wearing boots without nails to avoid splitting the grain, they generally worked in pairs, striking alternately with yard-long beater rods attached to the hand-staff of the flail by joints made of a loop of leather or eelskin. Their steady thumping was one of the regular winter noises in the quiet pre-mechanical countryside, and villagers said that they could tell by the sound how the work was paid – a slow, dull beat announced 'by the day, by the day', a brisker rhythm meant piecework, 'we took it, we took it, we took it'.

The thrashed grain was winnowed in the draught created by opening the central doors of the barn to separate grain from chaff and headcorn from tailcorn. Sometimes a shovel was used, sometimes a winnowing fan, a large two-handed basket in which the corn was first shaken to bring the chaff to the surface before it was thrown across the barn floor. The grain was finally winnowed again or sieved and was then ready for market or storage. Other tools used in the older barn routine included sheafbarrows, cornscoops, riddles and sieves, hummelers for removing the awns from barley and bushel measures and flat-edged boards called strikes for levelling the top of their contents to secure accurate measurement.

There were various attempts in the eighteenth century to mechanize thrashing, but the earlier inventors generally adopted the faulty principle of imitating human action and produced systems of mechanically-operated flails. One of these early machines, however, was sufficiently effective to survive to the days of electricity to which it was incongruously harnessed in 1932(33). It was not until 1786 that Andrew Meikle, a Scots millwright, developed the sounder technique, incorporated in all subsequent thrashing machines, of a drum with attachments revolving in a concave cover against which it beat and rubbed the grain off the straw, after which the grain fell into a container and the straw was carried away. He built as well as he designed – one of his machines which was in use until the 1920s is in the West Yorkshire Folk Museum.

The new invention replaced the flailers in barns and was at first driven either by manpower, waterpower or, more usually, by horses. Sometimes the horses turned wheelgear installed in special-purpose wheelhouses, sometimes portable wheelgear called 'farmers' wheels' because they were not part of the landlord's fixtures and could therefore be taken away by the tenant when he moved to another farm. A model of an 1830 outfit consisting of a three-horse wheel and a thrashing machine that could be dismantled and stowed on a waggon for easy transport can be seen at the Science Museum. By the 1840, however, horsepower was joined and increasingly replaced by steampower. By the 1850s steampower was in general use on the larger farms, and in 1867 the machinery judges of the Royal Agricultural Society of England discontinued prizes for horse-thrashers which they regarded as obsolete. The new machine had secured a new type of power.

Winnowing machines of sails attached to manually turned arms to create a draught were known in the eighteenth century, and by 1800 more developed forms of such equipment were being added to thrashing machines, although separate handdriven winnowing machines continued in decreasing use into late Victorian times and two which survived as working equipment into the 1960s are in the Museum of East Anglian Life(34). Seed dressers were later incorporated and then sacking mouths, so that by the 1850s the thrashing machine, although preserving its original name, had become a 'grain finishing' machine. The tasks of the farmer were further simplified in the next decade, when the agricultural engineering industry produced steamdriven and horsedriven elevators to stack the straw which accumulated at thrashing time.

Meanwhile a more radical change was taking place, for both steampower and thrashing machines became mobile. In the 1840s came the first portable thrashing machines of the type familiar to all those who remember farming in the days before the combine. At first these were driven by portable steam-engines which were also hauled to their place of work by horses, but later by self-propelled traction engines which could pull as well as drive. These developments met the needs of the farmer who preferred to take his machine to the cornstacks rather than bring all his corn to the barn. They also created a new form of enterprise for the contractor, and from mid-Victorian times onwards the arrival of the steam engine and its 'thrashing box' in the rickyard became a major annual occasion in many farm calendars(35).

But the older ways died hard. On some farms, flails were still in use in the 1930s, partly for thrashing small quantities of beans for feeding to horses or keeping as seed, partly for producing straw which could be used by thatchers, and the author was given a flail in 1942 by an elderly bailiff who made it 'from memory'. They may have lasted even longer in villages than on farms, for they were also used by cottagers who grew a little corn on their allotments(36).

A number of horsedriven thrashers, too, continued in service into the 1930s and 1940s and a few were converted to tractor-power or electric-power without passing through the steampower stage. But such equipment is easily scrapped and most of it had disappeared from farms before its memory had faded. In 1967 the author met an elderly Northumberland farmer who as a young man had trained horses for such work, and particularly remembered the ease with which they learnt to step over the revolving shaft on the ground that carried the power to the machine(37). The most obvious survivals of this technology are not mechanical but structural, the surviving wheelhouses described in the following chapter. Steam-engines also continued in service well into the age of the internal combustion engine. The last known example was a portable steam-engine which apparently powered a thrashing machine in the 1940s(38). The mechanical relics of steampower for thrashing are described later in this chapter and the structural relics in Chapter 9.

Harvesting and Stacking the Hay Crop

No haymaking machinery was exhibited at the first Royal Show which was held in 1839, because the grass crop was still cut by scythe, gathered into windrows by fork and rake, collected into haycocks by fork, then scattered to dry and recocked until it was ready to cart and stack. One by one, nearly all these operations were mechanized by horsedrawn equipment in the course of the next half century.

Locally manufactured horserakes and horsesweeps for collecting hay, and 'haymaking machines', generally called tedders from an old word for scattering or spreading, were known in the early nineteenth century and by the 1840s a variety of proprietary models of these machines were on the market. Horsedrawn mowers, similar in principle to the new reapers, appeared in the later 1850s and 30 years later the invention of the swathturner or side-delivery rake, which swept loose grass into windrows, completed the change from manpower to horsepower, except for loading and stacking. Horsedriven elevators were known in the later nineteenth century, but this form of labour-economizing equipment did not come into general use until the coming of cheap and portable mechanical power.

Samples of ricked hay were taken by a hay testing iron which was thrust into the rick and turned and twisted to catch a wisp of hay on its prongs. Such an iron could also be used to take the temperature of a rick suspected of heating. Hay which was sold off the farm was often prepared by itinerant haytiers, craftsmen immortalized by *The Mayor of Caster-bridge*. They cut the rick with a large, double-handed hayknife, formed it into trusses on a manually operated press they brought with them and bound them with hay bonds twisted together with a tool called a wimble(39).

Thatching

Some corn and hay were stored in barns. But most of these harvested crops were stacked in the open and thatched with straw, normally wheatstraw which is the toughest of cornstraws and so the least useful for feeding, to protect them from rain.

These stacks were sometimes thatched by professional thatchers accustomed to roofing houses and other buildings but often, since they were only temporary, by farmworkers who would not need the full set of thatching tools. A wooden yoke secured by a cord to carry straw, iron 'needles' to lever and hold the straw in position until it was pinned down by hazel spars, a mallet to drive in the spars, a rake to comb out the waste and an edging knife to trim the eaves and slope the sides of the rick inwards at the bottom to prevent rain running down them off the top were sufficient to make a roof that would last till the corn was thrashed or the hay fed(40).

Planting and Harvesting the Potato Crop

The potato crop is the most laborious of field enterprises, laborious to plant, laborious to harvest, laborious to sort. For more than half a century after its general introduction it was dependent on seasonal labour but when, in the late nineteenth century, this became less plentiful a combination of successful efforts achieved the mechanization of these processes in a few years. The horsedrawn mechanical planter developed in the 1850s which enabled seed to be dropped into furrows by a rotary feeding device, the horsedrawn mechanical digger with rotary forks which appeared in the 1870s and the mechanical riddle which appeared in the 1880s, all incorporated the principles on which subsequent developments were based. The story of potato mechanization, therefore, is short and lacking in tension, but the implements it produced were among the technical triumphs of the Victorian engineer(41).

Cidermaking

Until the end of the nineteenth century most cider was made on the farm from apples grown in the farm orchard. A primitive method of pulping the apples by hand in large mortars continued in parts of Wales into early Victorian times, and a wooden trough in which apples were pulped by two men working a roller is in the Welsh Folk Museum.

In the seventeenth century, however, the replacement of human by animal-power produced the prototype of the familiar cider mill in which the apples were crushed in a circular stone trough by a horsedriven runner stone, after which the juice was extracted from the pulp by a press worked by weights or a screw. Such mills and presses continued in use on many farms in the West Country into the early years of the present century, when cider production became a factory enterprise(42). A number survive, such as the seventeenth century press which continued in use until 1964 and is now at the Farm Museum, Redruth, Cornwall, and there is a fully equipped seventeenth century ciderhouse at the White House Country Museum, Aston Munslow, Shropshire. Less happy survivals are some of the old lead-lined presses which formerly caused a widespread form of lead-poisoning called 'Devon colic'. Once the source of the disease was identified, metal was removed from the presses and the disease disappeared. In the 1970s, however, a patient admitted to a Somerset hospital was found to be suffering from lead poisoning from homemade cider made in one of these ancient presses(43).

Livestock Production

Preparing Livestock Feed

The preparation of different kinds of feed for different kinds of livestock is one of the major continuing chores of the farmstead. Until the middle of the eighteenth century most of this work was done by hand with such tools as a heavy knife for cutting hay and straw into blocks convenient for handling. But in the next age new types of feed made new types of equipment necessary and a variety of new machines found their place in the barn.

The traditional bulky fodders, hay and straw, were commonly cut into short lengths and fed as chaff, since this made them more digestible and also saved waste at feeding time. The cutting box, the earliest form of chaffcutter, which consisted of a three-sided wooden box into which hay or straw was pressed by hand and then cut by a hinged knife at one end, appeared in the 1760s, continuing in widespread use for many years and, despite the development of more sophisticated factory-made equipment, in occasional use into modern times(44). One of these early chaffcutting boxes, which remained in service into the 1880s, can be seen at Pitstone Green Farm Museum, Bedfordshire, another, which continued in use into the present century, is in the Colchester and Essex Museum.

Meanwhile, the pioneers of the Agricultural Revolution were popularizing or introducing the rootcrops which provided succulent winter keep and thus helped to end dependence on hay for the winter feeding of ruminant livestock. This change in cropping systems meant change in the equipment of the farmstead, for turnips, swedes and mangolds were often fed sliced. This produced the billhook, a new form of handtool with a spiked instead of a curved end for picking up roots for cutting. It also produced handdriven rootcutters which by early Victorian times, when the feeding of roots was general practice, were part of the standard equipment of most farms.

These new machines contrast interestingly with a survival from the older agricultural order, the whinbruiser or gorse mill for pulping gorse gathered from the uncultivated heaths to supplement the precious store of winter fodder in the days before rootcrops or improved grasses. George Bourne, in his classic *Change in the Village,* mentions the gathering of furze from the common in the days before enclosure and chopping it for cows in what was apparently a chaffcutting box. As late as 1840 the Royal Agricultural Society of England offered a prize for a machine for cutting or chopping gorse, and pounded gorse was used as a feed in parts of Wales into the present century(45). An eighteenth century gorse mill and hooks and mallets for pressing gorse into chaffcutters are now at the Welsh Folk Museum.

Traditionally the farm also grew its own concentrate fodder, though little is known about early mills for cracking, bruising or grinding cereals, beans and peas. In the early nineteenth century, however, the coming of purchased concentrates in the form of linseed cake made necessary the invention of a new machine to reduce to manageable pieces the slabs in which it arrived. By the 1840s cakebreakers had duly appeared, produced by the developing industrial system to meet a need created by the developing commercial system.

In the next generation there was little technical development in this branch of farm equipment, although a predictable attempt was made on the larger farms to mechanize the preparation of livestock feed, using the power of the steam-engine to drive the factory-made machinery which ground or crushed corn and beans, broke oilcake and cut chaff and roots and its heat to steam potatoes and chaff, boil linseed and cook pigfeed. But the effort was premature, for the steam-engine was an expensive prime mover which required complicated systems of shafts and pulleys to distribute its power. The mechanization of fodder processing had to wait until the introduction into agriculture first of the internal combustion engine, then of electricity(46).

Milk Production

The most obvious relics of the older milking systems are the cowhouses, (described in Chapter 9) in which dairy herds were housed in winter and milked, originally by hand, all the year round. One type of cowhouse system, however, has now completely disappeared. This is town cow-keeping which supplied the townsman with milk from cows permanently housed in street dairies in the days before the railways made farm milk readily available and the enclosed urban herd became first a curiosity and then a memory. One of the few relics of this form of milk production to survive is a pair of cow hoof clippers which belonged to Charles Morley of Gallants Farm, Whetstone, now in Greater London, who in Edwardian times used to collect dry cows from the London cowhouses and take them back to his farm to be brought into milk again. The cows had, however, been confined so long and so closely that their hooves required trimming before they could be driven back to Whetstone(47).

The handmilker's personal equipment was simple, little more than a pail and a stool. The yoke with hanging pails in which he carried the milk to the dairy is familiar from many pictures and occasional memories, although it was probably out-lived by the backcan, a tin container specially shaped to fit the carrier's back which was used in some hilly areas. This survived in the Yorkshire Dales until shortly after the Second World War(48).

The change from handmilking to mechanical milking, which increases human productivity by enabling one man to milk more than one cow at once, was rapid and thorough. Forty years ago, less than one cow in six was milked by machine, but to-day the handmilker has joined the horseman and the flailer in history. The development of the milking machine, however, was slow and difficult since machine milking presents peculiar technical problems. Because the cow does not 'give' milk, it has to be extracted from her by applying to the milk in her teats sufficient pressure to overcome resistance at their orifices. There were many nineteenth century attempts to apply such pressures mechanically, sometimes by imitating the action of the milker who squeezes the teat, sometimes, more wisely, by imitating the action of the calf which sucks it. The modern milking machine is descended from the second type.

The first patent for a suction milking machine dates from 1831, but it was not until the end of the century that effective methods of applying a vacuum to the teat were developed. As a continuous vacuum causing a continuous flow of milk harms the cow, a rhythmic interruption of the vacuum by a period of atmospheric pressure was secured by a device called a pulsator, which was first used in the milking machine invented by Alexander Shields in 1895. A few years later the essential components of the modern milking plant were completed by the refinement, which further imitated the action of the calf, of alternating the vacuum with greater than atmospheric pressure. This was achieved by the teatcup, invented in 1903, which contains a flexible rubber lining so that pressure on the teat can be applied or released by the controlled admittance of air to the space between cup and lining.

The first generation of machines used in this country were literally milking machines which did no more than transfer the milk from the udder to a form of bucket. In the 1920s more sophisticated plant was developed. This carried the milk from the udder to the dairy in an overhead pipeline. It was this type of machine which made possible first the portable bail and then the ubiquitous milking parlour which are described in the following chapter(49).

Dairy Work
Evil communications do more than corrupt good manners. They also render impossible the general transport and sale of such a perishable commodity as liquid milk. Until the coming of the railways, therefore, dairy farmers sold their milk as butter or cheese, which were manufactured

in farmhouse dairies by the farmer's wife, his daughters and hired dairymaids.

Traditional buttermaking required pans, usually lead or lead-lined, where milk was left for the cream to rise, ladles or skimmers for removing the cream, churns in which it was worked into butter, wooden 'hands' for shaping it into blocks, and buttermoulds. There were two main types of churn, the plunger churn known in Tudor times, whose shape survived for the transport of liquid milk long after its use was abandoned on farms, and the end-over-end barrel churn which appeared in the eighteenth century. Both were usually worked by hand, but occasionally this laborious process was mechanized by horsedriven gear. An example of such equipment, installed in the early nineteenth century and used until 1879, can be seen in the Science Museum.

Cheesemaking was a more complicated enterprise and methods differed considerably from district to district. Essentially, it involved various forms of container and sieve, utensils or primitive mills to cut and break the curd at certain stages of manufacture, and substantial wooden vats in which the cheese was pressed, sometimes by presses using heavy stones, sometimes by screw presses or lever presses.

The ancient farm trades of buttermaking and cheesemaking gradually succumbed to the combined competition from their raw material and their finished products. On the one hand, the expansion of the liquid milk industry was made possible by the railway, easier by the lorry and essential by the depression of the late nineteenth and early twentieth centuries, when it became the only agricultural enterprise enjoying natural protection from the imports which ruined the traditional farming system. On the other, factories in this country and overseas offered the customer butter and cheese of standardized quality at prices which reflected economies of scale. By 1914 buttermaking on the farm survived only in a few areas where communications did not allow the marketing of liquid milk. By 1939 barely a thousand farms, using increasingly sophisticated methods, continued cheese production. Today about a tenth of the cheese made in this country comes from farmhouse enterprises, but these are essentially smallscale factories. The old ways are sometimes remembered, but no longer practised.

Some traditional dairy equipment was made on the farm, some by local craftsmen, very little, even in the last age of this domestic system, by the factory. For example, the mechanical separator, which removed the cream from the milk mechanically, did not appear until 1879. The design of the various utensils, in fact, was determined by local tradition and there was probably greater variation in detail between area and area than between century and century(50).

Sheep Farming

The shepherd's traditional equipment illustrates the nature of his work. The crook, his emblem, is essentially the individual tool of the individual craftsman and many of the iron heads, which in the nineteenth century increasingly replaced the old wooden heads, were made by the village blacksmith to the shepherd's own design. The portable hut in which he slept at lambing-time or the small brick shelters of the 'lookers', the contract shepherds of Kent and Sussex, which still stand like inexplicable privies in the remote levels of Romney Marsh, symbolized the loneliness of much of his working life. The bell he fastened around the neck of the leader of his flock and its 'sweet ringing', which is still occasionally remembered by elderly men, recall solitary shepherding on the unfenced heaths and uplands of a more primitive and more empty countryside. The iron bar with which he made holes in the ground for hurdles is a reminder of the intensive system of folding sheep on rootcrops which was one of the technical achievements of the Agricultural Revolution.

Nevertheless, the shepherd, like his colleagues on the farm, gradually accepted the products of the industrial age. The old scissor-action sheep shears of the type carved on the door of the church at Littlebury in Essex were replaced in the nineteenth century by factory-made shears of blades joined by a spring arc which were, in turn, rendered obsolete by the invention in 1877 of handdriven mechanical clippers working on the cutterbar principles. To-day such clippers are driven by electricity and the handdriven models are themselves historical survivals, occasionally demonstrated at agricultural shows. But handshearing still lingers in some remote areas(51).

There may also be occasional relics of an older and now forgotten economic order. In early mediaeval times sheep were primarily dairy animals and the milking of ewes continued long after the development of sheep as a source first of wool, then of meat. This practice, which involved the use of a form of headtie rather like a ladder, survived, surprisingly, almost to our own time and was not finally abandoned in Breconshire until the 1940s(52). An example of such a 'ladder' is preserved in the Welsh Folk Museum. A survival from an even older world, however, may still linger in the Lake District, where shepherds have traditionally used a dialect for counting sheep in which the numerals one, five and ten bear a marked similarity to those in Old Welsh, Cornish and Breton. Presumably counting in fives, using these numerals, dates from the days when Cumbria was part of the Celtic kingdom of Strathclyde(53).

Veterinary Work

Although the farrier and the 'cow-doctor' have a long history, farmers were once largely their own veterinary surgeons and they used on their stock treatments based sometimes on textbooks, sometimes on observation, sometimes on analogies from remedies applied to humans and sometimes on superstition. Thus, the manuscript horse-medicine book of Arthur Lake, a teamsman and a stallion-leader early this century, which is preserved in the Norfolk Rural Life Museum, includes a number of recipes which had been in his family for generations, some of them semi-magical in origin. Many farms, therefore, carried sets of primitive instruments, such as gelding and tail-docking irons, bleeding knives, teeth files, probes and drenching horns as well as branding irons to mark stock which grazed on common pastures with animals from other farms. In the nineteenth century all these gradually passed first to the attic and then to the museum as the trained practitioner assumed responsibility for the care of stock. The process of change from local self-sufficiency to reliance on outside resources is illustrated by the contrast between the tarbox or the salvebowl containing the homemade medicaments which the shepherd applied to his sheep and the tins of chemical preparation he has used since dipping to control sheepscab was made compulsory in 1905(54).

The limitations of traditional veterinary knowledge were strikingly illustrated in mid-Victorian times. As late as 1851, in the very year that the Great Exhibition proclaimed a new age of science and technology, Lakeland farmers during an epidemic of cattle disease drove their stock through the magic smoke of the Needfire which they lit by friction, after extinguishing all fires in their villages, in a ritual dimly remembered from the days of fireworship(55). A few years later a more general danger threatened the farmer's herds. This was the cattleplague or rinderpest, a virus disease which contemporary science could neither prevent nor cure. Introduced from Russia in 1865, it spread and killed rapidly until controlled by the restriction of movement and compulsory slaughter with compensation authorized by the Cattle Disease Prevention Act of 1866. In all, the plague caused the death of at least a twentieth of the nation's horned stock and in some areas, where up to two-thirds of the cattle were affected, losses were ruinous. The disaster left long memories – in the 1940s an Oxfordshire farmer showed the author a field on Otmoor where slaughtered cattle were buried in a mass grave. Its effects are recorded more permanently by gravestones or plaques on some Shropshire farms which commemorate the slaughter and burial of cattle there during the epidemic(56).

These two episodes provide a salutary reminder of the varied historical background to industrial archaeology. The Lakeland farmers looked to the remote past. The men who mastered the rinderpest prepared the way for the future, for the Cattle Plague Department of the Privy Council, which was established to adminster the Act of 1866, developed into the veterinary services of the present Ministry of Agriculture, Fisheries and Food(57).

Pest Control

Crops were traditionally protected from birds by scarecrows or, more effectively, by the efforts of small, cold and unhappy boys with handclappers, whose experiences left long and bitter memories. Significantly, George Edwards, the son of a Victorian farm worker who later became secretary of the Eastern Counties Agricultural Labourers' and Smallholders' Union and a Member of Parliament, called the autobiography he published in 1922 *From Crowscaring to Westminster,* and in 1971 a Gloucestershire cottager aged 92, recalling the misery of birdscaring, declared proudly that 'I swore none of my children would ever go birdscaring and they never did'(58).

Four-legged vermin required more drastic measures. Hunting is outside the scope of this book, but a number of early traps have survived. Some are in museums, but a few curious structural traps are still to be seen in the farmlands. The rabbit traps or 'smoots', small holes incorporated in drystone walls which allowed rabbits to pass through the wall to a trapdoor and a stonelined pit, were probably more to provide a dinner than control a pest. But the ingenious topless beehive 'goose bields' of the Lake District, into which the foxes were lured by a goose or other bait, and the stone traps operated by tripwires, which protected rabbit warrens on Dartmoor recall an early stage in pest control. In the days before organized foxhunting or shotguns, when the farmer built snares for the predators that threatened his stock from the only material his wild homeland offered. When guns became common, such traps were abandoned. On Dartmoor, however, occasional huts or screens of stone where the keeper could hide to shoot weasels and stoats in their breeding grounds survive to record the change in tactics in the endless war between the farmer and the enemies of the farm(59).

Farm Transport

The simplest form of farm transport is a combination of legs, back and some form of hold or container, such as the 'burden rope' looped around a bundle of hay or corn or the shoulderframe 'creels' for carrying small

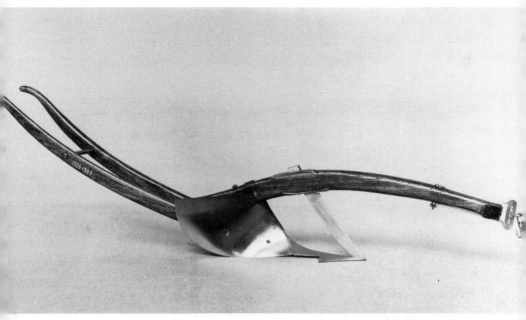

34 Small's plough, an improved design of the 1780s, showing the vertical coulter and the curved mouldboard which cut and overturn the soil. Compare this with the ard shown in figure 7.

35 The Kentish plough, one of the many local types of plough developed by local craftsmen in the days before the factory system.

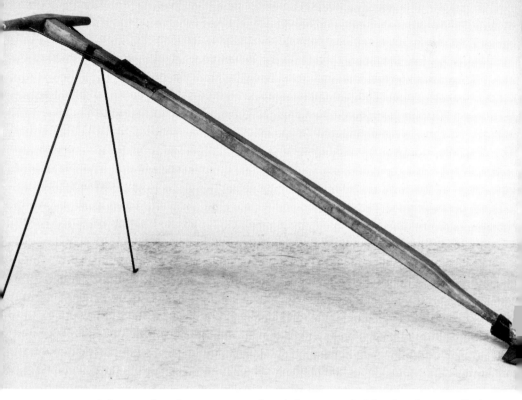

36 A breast plough, not a true plough but a spade laboriously propelled by the operator's padded thighs. A few were used on allotments in the present century.

37 A farm-made harrow of the type used from Tudor times to the introduction of factory-made equipment in the nineteenth century.

38   Seed fiddles, operated by a disk turned by a bow, were used for the sowing of small seeds. A few are still found in occasional use.

39   A drill, patented by James Cooke in 1782, which included the innovation of a system of small cups to feed the seeds into the tubes through which it reached the ground. It is not substantially different from the drill in use today.

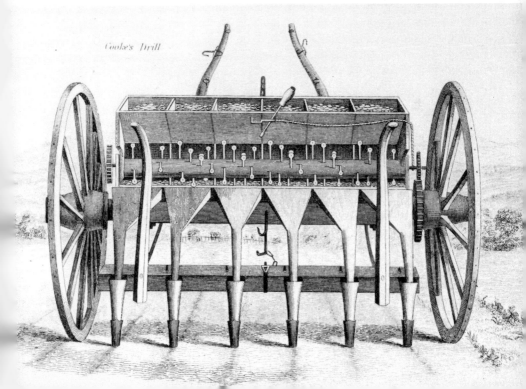

40 Sowing by hand or 'broadcasting' survived in some areas into our own age. This photograph was taken in Westmorland in 1952.

41 The older harvest. A reaper-and-binder at work.

42   One form of harvesting in the days before horsepower and machines replaced human muscles and hand-tools.

43   Thrashing by flail in the barn. The 'basket' on the left is a winnowing fan used for casting the grain into the air to separate from the chaff in the draught provided by opening the doors of the barn. The thrashing floor was commonly of oak planks or a mixture of earth, clay and dung beaten hard.

44　Early Victorian horse-thrashing gear. This type was called a 'farmer's wheel', as it was not a fixture and could be removed by the tenant when he moved to another farm.

45　Steam thrashing. This was often undertaken by contractors and the arrival of the steam engine and the 'thrashing box' was a major annual occasion in the older farm calender.

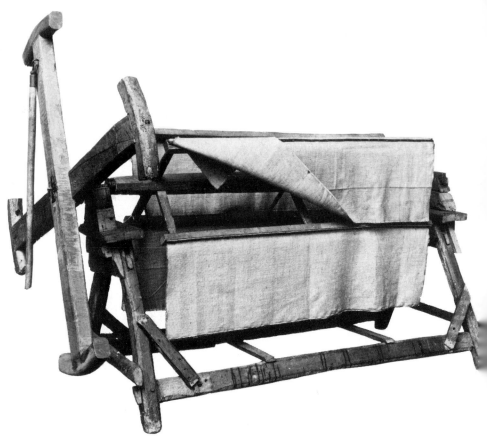

46 A hand-driven winnowing machine for use in the barn. It created a draught across which thrashed grain was cast to separate the grain from the chaff and headcorn from tailcorn. These machines were first used in the eighteenth century.

quantities of hay which in some hill districts have survived into our own age. So have the sledge, once the normal means of farm-carriage in some hilly areas, and the handbarrow(60). But over most of the country the farmer has traditionally relied for transport on the two-wheeled cart.

The cart has a long agricultural history. It has been used for many centuries for many purposes by farmers in many different areas, and many types were developed for particular purposes and specific needs. A curious example of a specialized local type of cart is the three-wheeled butt or durry, apparently peculiar to Devonshire, which was used for carting earth from the bottom to the top of steep fields. One such cart can be seen at the Alscott Farm Museum, Shebbear, North Devon. The lordly four-wheeled waggon, however, which has appeared in countless pictures of haytime and harvest in Olde England, was, historically, a recent addition to the farming scene and its operational career was short, less than two centuries from beginning to end.

Until the late eighteenth century, carts were the normal means of transport on the farm. But the new field system created by the enclosures, heavier crops and a general spirit of improvement combined to create a demand for some bigger and better means of carrying hay and corn from field to farmstead, from farmstead to market. So the village craftsmen applied themselves to meeting this need. In most parts of the country they took as their model the familiar carrier's waggon, which had been used for the haulage of goods since Tudor times, and produced the 'box waggon', so-called from the shape of its body. In the south-west, however, they developed a four-wheeled waggon from the two-wheeled harvest cart of the region and so produced the 'bow waggon', whose body rises gracefully above the front wheels. Thus arose the two main forms of the largest, most complicated and most enduring piece of mobile equipment used in farming before the coming of inorganic mechanical power.

In general, the new waggons were confined to the corn-growing areas of lowland Britain. They were uncommon in such grassland districts as the Cheshire Plain and in the uplands of the west, almost unknown in northern England, mountainous Wales and Scotland. In hilly and pastoral districts the cart continued unchallenged by its new rival.

Differing local circumstances produced differing local types of waggon. In East Anglia, for instance, they were large and boxlike, in the Cotswolds they were lighter and more manoeuvrable. Waggons designed for the Sussex clay country were fitted with broad wheels, those for downland chalk with narrow ones. Incidentally, Constable's famous Hay Wain can be identified as a type of waggon used in wooded areas, the body was removable so that the undercarriage could be used for carting timber.

Constable, a miller's son, had seen a good many waggons in his time and his hay wain was as real and precise as its landscape setting(61).

In the late nineteenth century the traditional types of local waggon were gradually replaced, either by the standardized designs mass-produced in factories which undersold the products of village workshops or by the cheap and durable Scotch cart, so-called because the first models came from factories in Scotland. A few country wheelwrights survived, but they, too, generally adopted factory principles and materials for their waggons and carts, so that even in isolated areas the manufacturer of bow waggons and box waggons had ended by the outbreak of the First World War. It was significant of the general change that the older vehicles were boarded with ash, poplar or elm, their successors with deal planks. The age of local materials, as of local skills, was over.

Waggon construction was one of the most exacting of all woodcrafts, for the huge vehicles required both strength and flexibility as they lurched over uneven fields or along rutted lanes with anything up to four tons of hay or corn aboard. Several hundred, including a South Midlands bow waggon, now preserved in the Museum of English Rural Life at Reading, which was used every year from 1838 to 1951, have survived to bear witness to the skill of their builders.

The last waggons went out of use in the 1950s. The working life of the humble cart was prolonged by the innovation of pneumatic tyres which were first fitted to cartwheels in the early 1930s. These eased the load and therefore reduced the advantage of the internal combustion engine over the horse(62). But the respite was only temporary and in the next decade cart and waggon together were replaced by tractor-drawn vehicles. A waggon used until 1955, and now in the Museum of English Rural Life, and a cart used until 1973, and now in the Welsh Folk Museum, were probably each the last of their kind(63).

Prime Movers

The Ox
Until the early Middle Ages the ox was the farmer's only draught animal and it was several centuries before it was finally replaced by the horse. Indeed, the comparison of the horse and the ox was a standard theme of agricultural literature from Tudor to Hanoverian times. Nevertheless, the ultimate victory of the horse was certain.

The ox, it is true, was cheaper to keep, it pulled more steadily, it was less liable to disease, while its skin was more valuable, its meat more attractive. The horse, however, had one supreme advantage, speed of working, and the farmer gradually accepted the necessity of paying the price of general utility for this increased ability to beat the weather. During the Agricultural Revolution many breeders improved the productivity of cattle, but none improved their draught power, and in Victorian times ox-teams became first .a rarity, then a curiosity. Nevertheless, a Welsh agricultural society offered prizes for the best yoke of ploughing oxen in 1877 and a few survived into the twentieth century(64). They seem to have lingered longest in Sussex, where the last horned team did not cease work until 1929, though the team of Lord Bathurst in Gloucestershire survived as a working unit drawing harrows and hauling timber until about 1945. By this time, however, they had ceased to be part of the farming economy and had become picturesque symbols of an older England(65).

Despite its long history, the working ox has left few relics, no more than occasional examples of the yokes or collars to which it was harnessed and of the shoes with which its cloven hooves were shod(66).

The Horse in the Field
Mediaeval, Tudor and Stuart farmers used the horse. The Hanoverians improved it and developed the three British breeds of heavy horse, the Clydesdale, the Shire and the Suffolk Punch. The Victorians made it the agent of a comprehensive process of mechanization.

The mechanization of fieldwork by animal power is, of course, as old as the plough team. But for many, many centuries ploughing and harrowing remained the only examples of such mechanization. As it was in the Iron Age, so it was in the days of Queen Anne. Corn was still sown, weeded and cut, hay still cut and turned, by the labour of men working with their hands or with tools which were extensions of their hands. But a great and revolutionary change began in the eighteenth century with the invention of the drill and the horsehoe and continued in the nineteenth with the invention of the reaper-and-binder, the mower and the swath-turner. All replaced the power of the man by the power of the horse and between them they wrought one of the greatest technical revolutions in agricultural history, the mechanization of the major routines of crop production which in the late nineteenth century required the muscles of over a million horses. There was sound technical reason behind the proud place of the Victorian horseman as the acknowledged aristocrat in the hierarchy of farmworkers.

In the early years of the next century came the introduction of the tractor, and in the next generation the old competition between horse and ox was repeated in new form. Like the ox, the horse had certain advantages. It was cheaper to buy and replace, cheaper to fuel, and it could work on wet, heavy land which defied the tractor. It was also, for some years, more reliable mechanically. But the tractor offered tireless speed which for the season-bound farmer outweighed all other arguments. In the 1930s the number of horses on British farms fell from 667,000 to 549,000, the number of tractors increased from 20,000 to 50,000. One final task, however, remained for the horse before it finally yielded to its rival. This was the contribution it made to the gigantic ploughing-up campaign of the Second World War. From the beginning the tractor did most of the work, but in the desperate early years the horse was its crucial ally, providing about one third of the farmer's total draught power. Later, as the pressures of war forced the pace of mechanization, this proportion sank first to a quarter, then to a sixth. So Dobbin earned his retirement; he had served his master faithfully in his time of greatest need.

To-day the horse has joined its old rival, the ox, in history, for the teams which still appear so gallantly at ploughing matches are generally sources of pride and pleasure rather than income to their owners. The true working horse is only found on a few farms where sentiment is supported by an appreciation of their value for certain limited types of job on certain types of soil or by the profits of a limited export market. Like the ox, it has left little evidence of its former importance. Significantly, however, this includes not only its working equipment, harness, shoes and grooming kit, but also the ornamental brasses with which proud owners used to decorate the gentle source of power on which their farming system depended(67).

Animal Power in the Farmstead

The use of the horse to drive thrashing machines and the relics in the farmstead of this technology together with its exceptional use to drive dairy machinery are described earlier in this chapter and in Chapter 9. A less familiar use of animal power in some Welsh farmsteads was the harnessing of donkeys or dogs on treadmills for such tasks as churning butter. A dogwheel in the Welsh Folk Museum recalls a practice which apparently survived into the early years of this century(68).

Water Power

Readers of the delightful *Carrington Diary* will remember Mr Deacon of Tewin Bury in Hertfordshire, who in the early 1800s 'turned the river by his wheat barn through the farme yarde for a thrashing macheen'. Many other farmers, particularly in Wales, harnessed convenient sources of this tireless prime mover to drive barn machinery and a recent survey in Somerset has identified the remains of 47 farm waterwheels and the dams, flumes or underground piping sometimes required to feed them. Two advanced nineteenth century landowners even installed water turbines on their farms. In general, however, waterpower has attracted less historical attention than other forms of farm power and less is known about its development and decline(69).

Steam Power in the Farmstead

The first steam-engine on a British farm was installed in 1798 by John Wilkinson, the ironmaster, to drive a static thrashing machine on his Denbighshire farm(70). Its successors on other farms in the next generation included what is now the oldest agricultural steam-engine in the world. This was built in 1812 by Richard Trevithick for a Cornish landowner, Sir Christopher Hawkins, and was so successful that a neighbouring landowner, Lord Dedunstanville, ordered another engine(71). The first engine, in which the boiler was replaced in 1856, and the boiler of the second engine are now in the Science Museum, London. Such early engines were installed primarily to drive thrashing machines, although some were also harnessed to other feed processing machinery. The first identifiable ancestor of general farmstead mechanization by inorganic power was a steam-engine erected in 1804 on a Norfolk farm where it drove a grinding mill and a chaffcutter as well as a thrashing machine(72).

This extension of use was prophetic, for in early Victorian times the steam-engine gradually changed its function. The development of portable thrashing machines, portable engines and traction engines rendered its original function in the farmstead obsolete and its power and heat were increasingly applied to fodder-processing. But the steam-engine did not prove a satisfactory agent for the comprehensive mechanization of the farmstead since it could not readily distribute the power it produced or apply it to haulage work. Its power contributed to the working of the farmstead processes but man remained the prime mover there.

The depression which began in the late nineteenth century ended the development of static steam power on the farm. It is unlikely that many steam-engines were installed after the 1870s, although a number continued in operation well into this century, when they were replaced, one by one, by internal combustion engines. They have, however, left few traces on the farm, although their memory is sometimes preserved by the chimneys which served them and the shape of the buildings (see Chapter 9) which housed them(73).

Steam Power in the Field

In 1767 Francis Moore patented 'a fire engine to supplant horses' with such confidence that he sold off all his horses and persuaded some of his friends to do the same in order to escape the fall in horse prices that would follow the inevitable triumph of steam(74). He was premature. Despite a number of later patents and inventions, it was not until 1836 that the first furrow was turned by a steam-hauled plough. This was powered by an engine on crawler tracks devised by John Heathcote, an appropriate ancestor for a twentieth century Minister of Agriculture. When stationary, it successfully pulled a plough by dragrope on a revolving drum.

Subsequent development was hindered by unsuccessful attempts to produce steamdriven rotary cultivators or steam-engines light enough for direct traction. But the future lay with the metal rope haulage of implements by stationary engines, a system greatly advanced by the development of steel rope which was far more effective than the clumsy chains or easily kinked iron rope previously used. Steel rope was first made by a Birmingham manufacturer in 1857 for John Fowler, a leading agricultural engineer, who in the following year won the prize long offered by the Royal Agricultural Society of England for an effective means of steam cultivation. His outfit, which is shown in a diorama at the Science Museum, consisted of an engine fitted with a haulage drum stationed at one side of the field opposite a self-propelling anchor and pulley on the other side. Together they hauled the plough or other implement across the field on an endless wire rope. A later and more common alternative to this system used two engines, one on either side of the field, each in turn hauling a reversible plough between them and both moving along the headland as each section was completed.

By 1867 well over 100 steam outfits, most of them owned by farmers, some owned by contractors, were at work. They used specially designed equipment heavier than any previously seen, six furrow ploughs which could turn more in an hour than a horse-team in a day, deepcutting drainage and subsoiling ploughs, massive cultivators and harrows and mole drainage units. Their main task, however, was ploughing, and it is significant that the memorial to Fowler, which stands in South Park, Darlington, shows one of his steam-ploughs.

The importance of the steam-plough decreased as the arable acreage shrank in the depression which began in late Victorian times, and in this century the tractor replaced the steam-engine in the field. But the victory of the internal combustion engine was slow. In the final year of the First World War steam-engines ploughed twice as many acres as tractors, in the early 1920s some 700 steam outfits were still at work, and the company which Fowler founded did not sell its last set of steam-ploughs in this country until 1923(75). Some outfits continued to be used in the 1930s and were joined in the Second World War by others brought out of retirement. The author remembers seeing one of them at work subsoiling on Henham Estate, Suffolk, in 1942. After the war decline was rapid. A crucial date in the process was 1960, when the last of the steam-ploughing contractors died at the age of 80 and his engines were sold. Significantly, in the same year steam-ploughs were used in a demonstration at the National Traction Engine Club rally at Appleford in Berkshire(76). Since then operational steam sets have owed their continued existence to the enthusiasm of their owners rather than to their economic merits(77).

The Internal Combusion Engine in the Farmstead

The internal combustion engine in static form appeared in the farmstead well before it appeared in mobile form in the fields and it wrought a greater revolution there. In the fields it replaced the animal power which by this time had replaced human power, but in the farmstead, where horses, waterwheels and steam-engines contributed only a small proportion of the total energy requirements, it commonly replaced human power without an intermediate stage.

Gas engines were used for farmstead work in the 1880s but were soon superseded by the 'petroleum engine' which made its earliest agricultural appearance at the Royal Show in 1888, and was recognized in the following decade as a serious rival to the steam-engine. In the next generation the use of this new prime mover spread rapidly. In 1908, it has been estimated, static petrol and oil engines provided the farming industry with 46,000 hp, in 1913 with 108,000 hp and in 1925 with 370,000 hp(78). By this time the static internal combustion engine was grinding and mixing fodder, milking cows and pumping water on a substantial and increasing number of farms.

Most of the early static engines have long since gone to the scrapheap. Such as survive illustrate a major and insufficiently appreciated stage in one of the most important of all technical changes in agriculture. Their function, however, also illustrates the limitations of mechanical power at that stage, for the internal combustion engine, like the steam-engine before it, failed to replace human muscles as power for the transport and handling of materials which form so large a proportion of farmstead chores. Manpower, by the 1930s relatively unimportant in the fields, continued as the major and literal prime mover in the operation of the farmstead(79).

The Internal Combustion Engine in the Field

The tractor, which is the only mobile machine thus powered within the present terms of reference, is a twentieth century creation and, mechanically, it can work for 40 years or more. So great is the speed of technical change, however, that the rate of obsolescence which threatened to destroy all the older generations of tractor has bred its own remedy. The few surviving early models are prized museum pieces, while more recent types are eagerly sought, restored and preserved by collectors. There is therefore a good deal of material available on the history of tractors in this country.

The tractor entered farming history in 1897, when one manufactured by a firm called Hornsby won a medal at the Royal Show, ploughed a field and was bought by a Surrey farmer in the first of all tractor sales. But the first effective tractor to be marketed was the Ivel, produced in 1902 by Dan Albone of Biggleswade, the son of a smallholder, who started his career as a motor mechanic and developed into a successful manufacturer of motorcycles and cars. The first Ivel ever built is in the Science Museum, and an Ivel which won the first prize at the 1903 Royal Show, and continued in use until 1940, is preserved in the private collection of Mr J.E. Moffitt, at West Side, Newton, Stocksfield, Northumberland. Within a quarter of a century the descendants of the Ivel had rendered steam-power obsolete for fieldwork and within half a century brought the age of the horse to an end. A significant date in this technical revolution was 1931, when the first British farms to be run without horses appeared, together with the phrase 'mechanized agriculture'(80).

At first engineers concentrated on improving the design and construction of the new machine in detail, decreasing weight, reducing fuel consumption, devising means of avoiding the worst consequences of mediocre maintenance and, above all, securing reliability. But later, more radically, they altered its character by adding to it the power-take-off, known in various early forms but finally developed in 1918 and standardized nine years later, which enabled it to drive equipment coupled to it. This equipment was at first usually a mobile implement, for example a mower, but the new device could also be used for static work, such as driving a tool for boring postholes. So the tractor began its conversion from an 'iron horse' which, like its organic predecessor, could do no more than pull, to a 'mobile toolbar' capable of being harnessed to an increasing variety of implements and equipment, including many which are not amenable to horizontal animal power.

This change, however, was gradual. In the 1930s the tractor was still mainly confined to field cultivations and to driving thrashing machines and mills. It was another 20 years before it became the maid-of-all-work we know today, although the next advance brought immediate benefits. In 1933 the first British tractors with pneumatic tyres were marketed, by 1939 nearly nine out of every ten tractors carried such tyres. The innovation increased speed of working, decreased fuel consumption and improved the comfort of the driver. But more fundamentally, it extended the scope of the tractor from fieldwork and limited static work to efficient general haulage, including haulage on the roads. The farmer had acquired a new power unit for transport.

In such general terms, the story of the tractor is fairly simple. In detail, however, it is complicated not only by the number of makes and models marketed and the specialized nature of many of the engineering developments, but also by the unfamiliar factor of overseas influences and products. For until this time the agricultural equipment used in Britain was made in Britain, only exceptionally owing anything to craftsmen or engineers elsewhere. But the tractor continued in dramatic new form the tradition established by the American reaper. The point was made obvious in the First World War when the infant industry founded by Albone proved unable to meet the sudden demand for fieldpower, and such British tractors as the Austin and Saunderson were joined by substantial imports of Mogul, Titan and Fordson tractors from the USA.

Indeed, after the war, most of Britain's tractors came from America until 1933, when the Ford Motor Company began the large-scale production of tractors at Dagenham. Significantly, the power-take-off, pneumatic tyres, the rowcrop tractor, the diesel engine and the track-laying or crawler tractor all originated in the USA. Again, as early as 1917 the Fordson, which was to prove one of the most successful of all interwar tractors, foreshadowed the mechanical future with its unit construction of engine, gearbox and final drive and its general simplicity and accessibility. American technology and American machines are integral parts of this section of British agricultural history.

So the tractor of the 1930s differed greatly in function as well as mechanical competence from its ancestors early in the century. But it was still no more than a basis for continuing improvements, notably the introduction in this decade of Ferguson's 'three point linkage' system which reduced weight, improved stability and secured greater control of operations by integrating tractor and implement into one unit. Today a prototype Ferguson of 1935 stands alongside a Fordson of 1917 and an Ivel of 1902 in the Science Museum. Many other historical models of different types and ages, including what is probably the first electric tractor in regular farm use, built in 1948 and now preserved in the Lackham Agricultural Museum in Wiltshire, can be seen in collections and demonstrations of old tractors to illustrate stages in the development of the versatile machine on which the modern farmer depends(81).

9

Farm Buildings

'Structural Documents'

The industrial buildings of the farm are among the most conspicuous objects in the agricultural landscape. To the industrial archaeologist they are also among the most interesting, for few other industries can show such a continuous and comprehensive series of buildings with which to illustrate their past.

Indeed, this historical legacy is itself a product of a period of drastic agricultural change, the depression which began in the last decades of the nineteenth century and lasted until the Second World War. This ended the orderly process of farmstead development and left a lifetime's arrears of modernization which the present age is still making good. Recently, it is true, the piecemeal adaptations and improvements of immediate postwar years, which preserved much of the old pattern of the farmstead and many of the buildings which composed it, has given way to more comprehensive demolition and new construction. Even so, most farmers have inherited more buildings than they have erected. The Oxfordshire farmstead which includes a seventeenth century barn, a seventeenth century dairy block with a sign over the door exempting it from the Window Tax, an eighteenth century barn, a nineteenth century cartshed and various twentieth century buildings provides no more than an unusually comprehensive example of a fairly common type of survival. Mediaeval and Tudor buildings may be individual rarities, but Hanoverian and Victorian work still provides about a third of the farmer's building stock(1).

The economic disadvantages of such obsolete equipment are obvious. But the farmer's embarrassment is the industrial archaeologist's opportunity, for in various ways these old buildings and their relationships to each other in the farmstead of which they are the component parts record with particular clarity a great deal of rural history.

They preserve the imprint of the farming technologies and systems for which they were designed; they illustrate the building materials and methods of their time; and the manner in which so many have been adapted to new purposes reflect the changes which have come to agriculture and to the industries which serve it. Further, those built in the eighteenth and nineteenth centuries demonstrate the working of the landlord-and-tenant system, which has played so important a part in agricultural history, for in this period few farmers owned the land they worked and the erection of buildings was the responsibility of the landowner. And all around them soils and slopes, streams and springs, suggest the reasons why their founders, from Saxon peasant to Victorian landlord, chose the site on which they or their successors stand. In general terms, therefore, they make manifest the physical and historical variety of the landscape, the sequence of changing agricultural needs and the different ways in which different men at different times have used the resources and skills available to them. They are, indeed, rightly described as 'the structural documents of farming history'(2).

The Longhouse

The oldest type of farm building to survive into the present century combines dwelling house and livestock accommodation under one roof. This is the longhouse, essentially a rectangular structure in which the farmer and his family live at one end, his inwintered stock at the other. This type of building has served more generations of farmers in this country than any other and only in our own century has it ceased to provide shelter for man and beast, yet few modern visitors to the countryside are aware that it ever existed.

The ancestry of the longhouse goes back to Neolithic times and archaeological and documentary evidence shows that it survived in the lowlands until the end of the Middle Ages, after which the separation of domestic and industrial buildings became the rule. Possibly the poorer peasantry continued to live in such houses while their more prosperous brethren lived more comfortably in houses standing apart from the service buildings, but the old system was gradually abandoned as living standards improved. The protection it gave and the warmth it conserved ensured its continuance in various upland areas, though even here the new influences were spreading. In surviving examples of longhouses on Dartmoor and in Cumberland which date from Stuart times, there is no direct communication between the two parts of the building, while the recent excavation of the longhouse village of West Whelpington in Northumberland shows that originally the inhabitants were separated from their animals only by paving stones, then by partitions and finally, by the seventeenth century, by walls which ended internal access between living room and cowhouse.

The same distinction between living quarters and livestock accommodation is found in Cumberland in certain horizontal versions of the longhouse of the same period. These were built into the hillside and housed cattle on the ground floor, the family on the first floor. A curious local continuation of such two-storey housing is the 'bastle' of the northern border counties which was built to provide protection for men and animals from Scots raiders. The tradition continued long after the military need had passed into history and one bastle was built as late as 1811. But this is an exceptional survival in an exceptional area(3).

Longhouses had ceased to be built in the West Country by the end of the seventeenth century. Various types of farmstead which housed people and animals under the same roof, though separated by a doorless partition, continued in the northern and Welsh uplands and longhouses were still being built in Northumberland in the early nineteenth century. One version of this system was the Yorkshire laithe house, with dwelling, barn and byre under one roof. The first of these was built about 1650 and the last in 1880.

By the early twentieth century, however, the number of occupied longhouses even in remote areas of Wales was falling rapidly, mainly because of the requirements of sanitary legislation, and the next century saw the end of this ancient tradition. A few longhouses in Wales, Devon and Cornwall were inhabited after the Second World War, sometimes as late as the 1960s, and one dating from about 1600 was in use in a Dorset village in the 1970s. But today, apart from any such exceptional survivals, all longhouse structures, including certain granite buildings apparently of longhouse type on the fringes of Dartmoor which may date from the original colonization of these uplands in the thirteenth century, have now been converted to farmhouses or farm buildings(4).

Archaeologists excavate the remains of longhouses from time to time, but the best places to see examples of this primitive but convenient homestead are the open-air museums. There is a rare example of a lowland longhouse, which includes a fireplace added in the family part of the building in the sixteenth century, at Castle Farm Folk Museum, near Bath, and a fifteenth century example from Denbighshire and an early eighteenth century example from Radnorshire at the Welsh Folk Museum.

'Welsh Pigsties' and Yorkshire Potato Cellars

Another structural tradition from times beyond the written record may be preserved by some 40 conical 'pigsties', mainly in Wales, and occasional potato cellars in the Yorkshire Dales, whose design and corbelled stonework suggest a connection with the ancient beehive huts of Wales, Scotland and Ireland. None of these curious structures can be dated and nothing is known about their history. But it is not impossible that farmers continued to use this simple and traditional method of construction for housing their crops and stock long after they and their families had developed more comfortable homes(5).

Corndrying Kilns

The complex installations which dry the sudden mass of grain delivered by the combine at harvest time to a moisture content allowing safe storage are newcomers to the farm. But they have various ancestors there, going back to the Roman corndrying kiln, found at Foxholes Farm in Hertfordshire and restored by the Hertfordshire Museum, in which corn cut green was dried. A number of mediaeval and later kilns, some apparently used up to the eighteenth century, have been excavated on farm sites in the wetter areas of the country and occasional examples with drying chambers floored with stone or slate grills or perforated tiles above heating chambers can be found in the Lake District(6).

The Corn Barn and the Wheelhouse

The corn barn remains one of the most obvious and familiar of all farm buildings. It has now been obsolete for a century and a half but it still continues to dominate many farmsteads as it has done since the days of the Plantagenets.

The standardized pattern of the barn was determined by the storage and processing needs of the corn harvest and was established certainly by the twelfth century, when the first description of such a building occurs in the written record, and probably a good deal earlier. In its simplest form, a barn consists of two end bays separated by a central passage served by two pairs of double doors in opposite walls with a hard floor between them. At harvest time, packhorses, carts or waggons entered the barn through one door, unloaded their sheaves and left by the other door. Then, in the winter, these sheaves were taken down from the dark ends of the barn for thrashing by flail and winnowing in the draught between the open doors.

Large barns had two thrashing floors and two sets of doors. Large farms had two barns, one for the wheat which was sold off the farm, one for the oats and barley which were fed on it. But they were all planned on the same principles for the same purposes, apart from an interesting exception to this general rule. In 1792 a visitor to the West Country found builders cutting large new doors into the massive mediaeval walls of Buckland Abbey barn 'with a labour equal to that of cutting solid rock'. For the barn dated from the days of 'packhorse husbandry', when corn was brought from the hilly harvestfields on horseback, and the doors sufficient for such primitive transport were not sufficient for waggons which carried the heavier harvests of an improved farming system. This is the first recorded instance of the adaptation of old farm buildings to new farm needs and it illustrates a tradition which gives farm buildings much of their value for industrial archaeologists(7).

Most of the barns which stand on farms today date from the seventeenth, eighteenth or early nineteenth centuries. But some earlier examples are found, including most of the few mediaeval farm buildings to survive. Among these are the huge and gracious barns commonly, though sometimes wrongly, described as 'tithe barns', a term rightly applied to barns built on ecclesiastical estates to store tithes or other dues paid in corn, but often casually applied to all mediaeval barns. The barns of the churchmen, however, were exceptional in size and structure and they tell us little about the normal farm barns of their time. Some, indeed, were only partly farm buildings. They were also the central depots of huge agricultural enterprises and their descendants include merchants' warehouses as well as farmers' grainstores. The room over the porch at the monastic barn at Bredon in Worcestershire, which served as office and living quarters for the monk or bailiff in charge of the farm, illustrates the managerial resources of the organizations which planned and operated the farming empires of which these huge buildings formed part(8).

The barn was rendered obsolete by technical development, the mechanization of the thrashing and winnowing processes around which it was designed. At first, in the later years of George III's reign, the change was slight. Some of the early thrashing machines, which were driven by horses or, less frequently, by water, could be fitted into existing barns with little difficulty. Others were housed in new barns, in general similar to the traditional type, but smaller since the thrashing machines required less height than the swinging flail and the winnowing machine less floor space than manual winnowing. But the new thrashing technique also produced a less precedented type of building, the wheelhouse, a single-storey round, square or polygonal building, between 15 and 30 feet in diameter, with a conical or pyramidal roof. These wheelhouses, which stood adjacent to the barns they served, protected the overhead wheels, the shafts that drove the thrashing machines and sometimes the fodder-processing equipment in the barn, and the circumambulatory horses that powered them.

Wheelhouses were known in most parts of the country, although they were rare in Wales where waterpower was widely available, but were concentrated for climatic reasons in the north-east and in the West Country. In the north they were commonly known as gingangs, in the west as pound houses as the barn machinery which they drove often included the cider mill which crushed the cider apples. Most of them were built between 1800 and 1850, by which time steampower was replacing horsepower. A few, however, were built in the following years and one in Yorkshire as late as the 1870s or early 1880s. Many continued in use into this century and one even into the 1930s.

Today most of the wheels and associated equipment have disappeared, but some 1,300 wheelhouses survive on the farms of England, Wales and Scotland. A gingang, complete with a horsewheel dating from the 1830s, can be seen at the Beamish North of England Open Air Museum and a pound house at Alscott Farm Museum at Shebbear in North Devon(9).

In early Victorian times the steam-engine began to replace the horse and the waterwheel even as they had replaced the human flailer, and the long reign of the barn ended in a generation. The steam-engine soon became normal equipment on the larger and more advanced arable farms and to this day some of the factory-type chimneys built to serve this new form of barn-power still stand incongruously amid the fields as memorials to the first introduction to agriculture of an inorganic prime mover(10). Nevertheless, 'the steam-driven barn' did not last long, for the convenience of taking the thrashing machine to the corn stacks instead of bringing all the corn to the barn encouraged the development of portable thrashing machines hauled and driven by steam-engines. As the years passed, more corn was thrashed in the fields and there was less need for the traditional type of barn. After the 1850s, therefore, new barns were designed for storing and processing not the corn crop but homegrown and purchased fodder for livestock and so became minor milling and mixing factories. The long life of the corn barn was over, though, astonishingly, one of the traditional type was built in Staffordshire in the 1880s and another, at Mendlesham in Suffolk, as late as 1894, both apparently designed for flail thrashing(11). Apart from such anachronisms, however, no more corn barns were built and existing barns were gradually adapted to other purposes, such as the preparation of livestock feed, or allowed to degenerate into dignified dumps for anything that could not be more conveniently stored elsewhere.

All corn barns served the same crop and all illustrate some aspect of a major agricultural theme. But many also tell their own particular stories.

Sometimes, the interest is general, like that of the massive flint barns along the base of the escarpment near Eastbourne which once housed the harvests of large ecclesiastical estates farmed in hand, 'monuments to the great scale and bountifulness' of these mediaeval model farms. Sometimes their interest is purely local. Mortimer's Barn at Foxton in Cambridge-shire was six centuries old when it was pulled down a few years ago, but it preserved to the end the name of a family whose male line ended in Plantagenet times, while terracotta roundels on the brickwork gables of a barn at Kelsale in Suffolk show the rampant lions of the Mowbrays and the Bigods before them(12). And sometimes the interest is almost personal, like the rapport felt by the modern visitor to the barn at Arkley near Barnet on the north-western outskirts of London with two unknown men who left their marks there, one who carved 'WB 1786' on the main beam of a truss, the other who fixed a little platform under the ridge as a nesting place to encourage the owls that ate the rodents that ate his grain. The latter, however, may reflect specific historical change as well as a general hazard, for rat control became crucial after the invasion of this country by the brown Norway rats which began about 1730. It is probable that many of the owlholes in barns date from the eighteenth and nineteenth centuries(13).

Barns are probably the most common of all old farm buildings, certainly the most common from the earlier centuries, and they are well represented in the open-air-museums. One or two, indeed, like the tithe barn at Bradford-on-Avon, which as late as the 1940s continued in comprehensive agricultural use, housing two tractors, purchased feed-stuffs, hay and straw, eight horses and a hundred pigs, now provide appropriate shelter for collections of farming bygones. A number, too, have been converted to dwelling houses, halls or, like the two sixteenth century barns at Knebworth House in Hertfordshire, into cafeterias for country parks. On farms, however, they are decreasing in number, for they are expensive to maintain and their agricultural value is small, although in the last generation some have recovered part of their ancient purpose. They now house the complicated equipment needed for drying and storing grain from the combine-harvester. So part of the harvest routine has returned in new form to its ancient home. Nevertheless, we must beware of any sentimental assumptions of continuity. It was mere structural accident that a building designed for the processes of one age happened to be available and suitable for the process of another(14).

The Granary

Thrashed grain required safe storage, for it was both the farmer's main cash crop and the seed for his future corn crops. Some farmers stored it in the barn or, to save it from damp, in the top storey of a two-storey farm building. Lofts over cowhouses or stables were sometimes used, but lofts over implement sheds were preferred because there was then no danger of contamination by foul air rising from the animals below. An interesting eighteenth century granary standing over an implement shed is preserved at the Avoncroft Museum of Buildings. With its kennels under the stairs for the dogs which discouraged thieves and rats and its ladder rack under the eaves, this building gives an agreeable impression of careful planning. But, like other two-storey granaries, it also gives a less agreeable impression of the physical demands of the pre-mechanical farmstead on the farmer and his men, who had to carry the corn harvest on their backs in a succession of hundredweight sacks up a flight of steps.

Other farmers, however, built special granaries, small, rectangular buildings, often resting (like some ricks) on mushroom-shaped staddle-stones to protect the corn from rats and mice, which could be conveniently supervised and kept locked. Such granaries go back to Tudor times and were in widespread use in southern England by the eighteenth century. Examples dating from the sixteenth to the nineteenth centuries can be seen at Lackham Agricultural Museum in Wiltshire and in the Weald and Downland Open Air Museum.

Others remain on modern farms, contrasting pleasantly with the concrete and asbestos-cement buildings around them, for the farmer finds them useful stores for seeds, tools or spare parts. Many staddle-stones from dismantled granaries or from rickyards also survive, though less agriculturally, for they have changed from farmyard equipment to garden ornaments(15).

Haybarn and Dutch Barn

Traditionally hay was stored either in ricks or in well-ventilated barns. The ancestor of the modern Dutch barn, which now protects a variety of farm produce and equipment as well as hay, was a set of uprights with an adjustable roof which Sir Hugh Plat noticed in Holland in the sixteenth century and introduced to this country. But it was not until the later years of George III's reign that farmers began to make general use of a more practical version of this design in which the cumbersome and relatively fragile moveable roof was replaced by a fixed one.

Such skeleton structures of local timber or stone or brick pillars roofed with thatch or tiles soon proved their value as alternatives to the seasonal thatching of cornstacks and haystacks and were widely used for the storage of hay, since they gave better ventilation than an enclosed building. The nineteenth century haysheds with pillars of local slate which can be seen at the Welsh Folk Museum, for example, were built to house the increased hay crop which followed the draining of the Dwyryd valley. In due process of industrial time, this simple design offered manufacturers the attractive combination of a standardized structure and a substantial and continuing market. In the 1880s the Dutch barn became the first agricultural building to be successfully prefabricated, and by Edwardian times it had established itself as one of the normal features of the twentieth century farming landscape(16).

Silos

Silos in their modern form are recent arrivals in the countryside. But silage-making, which preserves grass for feeding in the winter by a crude form of canning in some form of structure, has a long and curious history.

The technique was developed on the Continent in the middle years of the nineteenth century. It was introduced to this country about 1880, in the early days of the agricultural depression when farmers turning from corn to livestock production sought some form of winter fodder cheaper to grow than roots and more reliable than hay, which has to be cut, dried and stacked in a peculiarly unpredictable climate. At first, development was in the hands of major landowners, the usual leaders of the farming industry, but already the shape of things to come was apparent. In the 1880s two substantial official reports on the new techniques and the structures they required helped to make the early methods of silage-making one of the best documented of all farmstead developments and marked the first appearance of the government in its now familiar role as agricultural investigator and advisor.

This introduction, however, failed, largely because of insufficient research on the biological processes involved, and by the end of the century most of the varied form of silos used had been abandoned. The next age saw a new and more scientific approach and by the 1930s a number of tower silos of timber, brick, steel or concrete erected by advanced farmers, were giving satisfactory performance and allowing their users to accumulate the experience which made possible the rapid expansion of silage-making in the next generation.

A horizontal silo, which was built on a Herefordshire farm in 1885, was still in use in the 1960s and now serves as a manure store, is probably the oldest silo in the country, although there may be other unrecorded survivals from the first generation of silos elsewhere. Many of the steel and timber towers of the interwar period, too, have now disappeared. But a number of brick and concrete ones still stand as witnesses to a stage in the development of a technique which was one of the last to be pioneered by the traditional leaders of agriculture and became one of the first research-based systems to affect the design of the farmstead(17).

Cartsheds and Implement Sheds

Carts and waggons were substantial and expensive items of farm equipment. So it was always worth the farmer's while to house them in, for example, open-sided lean-to sheds or the 'shroff huts' of undressed timber uprights roofed with brushwood and thatched with straw traditional to Suffolk, to protect them from the sun and rain which warped and rotted their timbers. Such buildings provide useful evidence of the size of farms and types of farming in particular areas at particular times. They also sometimes provide interesting sidelights on local development. In some parts of North Wales, for example, most cartsheds date from the nineteenth century, since until that time sledges were the normal means of transport and these required less substantial protection.

Cartsheds probably also housed the more important of the simple field implements of pre-mechanical times. But in the nineteenth century the increasing complication and value of field machinery made necessary better and larger implement houses with stores for tools and spare parts. Few of the older cartsheds and implement sheds survive, for they are too small for modern equipment. Such as do remain provide an interesting commentary on the mechanization of agriculture. One local survey of buildings erected before 1880, for instance, found examples of cartsheds dating from at least the middle of the eighteenth century and tool-sheds with lockable doors dating from the 1850s. Further study would have continued the story to the larger sheds with wider bays for the tractors and combine-harvesters of today(18).

Cattle Yards and Cattle Buildings

The simplest form of cattle accommodation is the open yard. Sometimes such yards are truly open, sometimes they are provided along one or two sides with shelters such as 'hovels' of the type shown at the Weald and Downland Open Air Museum or the two-storey linhays of Devonshire in which hay is stored in the tallet or upper floor. This corruption of *tabulatum* presumably passed from mediaeval Latin into local dialect(19). Such yards, in which inwintered livestock tread straw into manure, have long formed the centre of farmsteads in most areas of this country and many still survive in their traditional form. In general, it is likely that the larger the yard, the later it was built, for the increase in the number of cattle which followed the general cultivation of the new foddercrops of the Agricultural Revolution continued in the nineteenth century and the development of cattle accommodation was a major preoccupation of the Victorians. Their yards grew in size until they sometimes covered far more floorspace than the whole of the rest of the farmstead, though they were often subdivided for convenience of feeding, the welfare of the animals and the economy of straw.

The Victorians, however, improved the efficiency of yards as well as increasing their size. For the practice of roofing yards, which developed in mid-Victorian times, reflected more than the recognition that the improved cattle of the period required improved housing if they were to repay the time and skill invested in them by those who had bred and developed them. It also reflected the growing importance of a relatively new addition to farming resources, purchased concentrate feedstuffs, originally produced in this country but later imported.

First used in the late eighteenth century, these feeds were to make possible in the early twentieth century an unprecedented agricultural partnership in which the home farmer provided buildings and livestock and the overseas producer a steady supply of concentrate feedstuffs which passed through the farmstead to emerge as meat, milk and manure. In Victorian times, their effects were less pervasive, but the widespread use of such expensive materials, notably the linseed cake so prized for putting flesh and bloom on fattening bullocks, increased the incentive to provide stock with conditions which encouraged the efficient conversion of feed into meat or milk. In addition, less obviously, it increased the incentive to provide better protection for manure to prevent the wastage of the residues of these rich rations by exposure to the elements.

Of course, observant farmers had long known that manure exposed to rain and sun lost much of its value. The Victorians, however, were the first who could measure such losses and draw informed financial and structural conclusions from their figures. In the 1850s Voelcker, the agricultural chemist, had shown by a series of experiments the degree to which cover preserved the nutritive value of manure and in due course the covered yard became in most areas one of the most conspicuous signs of progressive estate management. This was the first contribution of the scientist to the principles of farm building design and it was many years before Voelcker's successors continued the tradition he founded. But the historical importance of his work is as obvious to later generations as its practical importance was to his contemporaries(20)

The Victorian improvement of the yard, which is essentially an extensive system of housing, was accompanied by an increase in more intensive systems of boxes or stalls in which cattle were fattened individually or in small groups. Such systems provided cattle with the most favourable conditions for meat production and farmers with the most effective method of manure conservation so far devised. They were, however, costly in both capital and labour and the fattening boxes that survive, such as those at Egmere Farm, near Walsingham on the

Holkham estate in Norfolk, which was completed in 1857, reflect the combination of wealth, managerial efficiency, confidence and low wages so typical of mid-Victorian agriculture(21).

A more familiar type of cattle accommodation is the cowhouse, cowshed or byre in which cows are housed in winter and milked all the year round. The basic pattern of mangers, standings and passages in such buildings is determined by a combination of the needs of the cow and the needs of the milker and, predictably, has changed little down the generations. The earliest surviving cowhouses, which date from the seventeenth century, are the recognizable ancestors of their twentieth century descendants. But it was a long time before such familiar components of the modern cowhouse as sloping standings, chain-ties, divisions between cows, internal water-supplies, feeding passages and dungchannels falling to grated outlets, which were all known in advanced cowhouses in the early 1800s, became general practice. The gradual improvements in detailed design and equipment reflect the growing appreciation of the importance of hygiene and convenience, the use of new building materials and manufactured equipment, greater attention to the feeding of the cattle which made feed preparation rooms an integral part of many cowhouse systems and, above all, the effects of legislation.

The development of the railways made farm-produced milk an increasingly important item in urban diet and governments, in an age in which Disraeli took *'Sanitas sanitatum, omnia sanitas'* as the text of one of his most famous speeches, were not likely to overlook the dangers inherent in a highly perishable commodity peculiarly susceptible to contamination. Consequently, a series of measures, beginning with the Dairies, Cowsheds and Milkshops Order of 1885, empowered local authorities to issue by-laws to ensure healthy cattle and clean milk. Over the years the local councils developed codes and practices to establish standards of lighting, ventilation, drainage and water-supply, to replace earthen and cobble floors by concrete floors, hopeful slopes by dungchannels and cows standing head to head by cows standing tail to tail to prevent cross-infection. None of these improvements, taken individually, revolutionized the cowhouse. Taken together, they created a new form of an old building(22).

Meanwhile, however, new equipment was producing a new type of milking installation. In the 1920s A.J. Hosier, a Wiltshire farmer, transferred milking machines previously used in cowhouses into portable structures called bails, best described as milking machines on wheels, in which he milked his cows that grazed the chalk downs all the year round. In 1932 he established a fixed milking-point on his farm and so converted the portable bail into the first milking parlour, 'a housed milking machine', from which are descended the parlours in which most cows are now milked. The system he founded has also sometimes given a new purpose to old yards in which the cows formerly housed in cowhouses are now wintered. Yet so great is the speed of change that some early types of parlour are now historic and men who can remember the bail as an innovation can see an early model preserved at the Castle Farm Folk Museum near Bath(23).

A curious by-product of the expansion of the rural liquid milk industry was the disappearance of the enclosed urban dairy herds which had for so long provided the townsman with his daily milk, but which could not withstand the competition of farm milk and the demands of sanitary legislation. The old system died hard. As late as 1930 there were just over a thousand cows in inner London, nearly five thousand in Liverpool, and the last cow was not milked in the City of London until the early 1950s, the last cow in Liverpool, incidentally from a herd fed in summertime on grass cut from Everton Football Club's training ground, not until 1975. But today it is barely a memory, with few relics left for the industrial archaeologist(24).

The Dairy

Originally, all farm dairies were in the farmhouse, large, stone-floored rooms where, with laborious traditional skills, the farmer's wife, daughters and maidservants processed milk into butter or cheese. A substantial butter dairy would contain a milk room, a churning room and a room for the storage of utensils, while a substantial cheese dairy would contain a milk room, a scalding and pressing room and a salting room in addition to a ventilated chamber or loft where the cheeses ripened in storage. Such dairies occupied much of the farmer's home, as befitted the workshops of a major domestic industry whose importance was recognized by legislative exemption from the Window Tax which was imposed from 1795 to 1851. Such exemption was dependent on the clear marking of the windows as 'Dairy' or 'Cheese room' and the occasional inscriptions which survive over windows which now serve domestic rooms are among the relics of this ancient trade.

In the late nineteenth and early twentieth centuries the farmhouse butter and cheese industries gradually succumbed to the competition of imported dairy produce and the developing liquid milk enterprise, and today butter-making is merely a memory and cheese-making survives only on a few highly specialized farms. But the ancient trades have left their structural legacies on many farms in the old dairy areas. A survey a few years ago found some 350 farmhouses in the Vale of Gloucestershire and 50 in Wiltshire which still contained cheese lofts, sometimes with the original louvred windows, and suggested that there were probably a number of similar survivals in Somerset, Herefordshire and Worcestershire. One of the Gloucestershire farmhouses was dated 1863 and must, therefore, have been among the last dairy farmhouses to be built(25).

Frequently, however, these old farmhouse dairies created new problems. The dairy farmer naturally continued to use the dairy in the farmhouse, weighing, cooling and storing his milk in the farmhouse rooms where his mother and grandmother had once made butter and cheese. Such dairies were commonly some distance from the cowhouse and the milk was too often exposed to contamination in the yards across which it was carried in pails. But it took many regulations, many arguments and many years to end this old tradition and establish the new type of dairy adjacent to the cowhouse it served. The change is difficult to follow in detail, but it was apparently the replacement of the older regulations by the more demanding Milk and Dairies Order of 1926 that finally established the dairy with its corrugated cooler, washing troughs and sterilizing chest as part of the cowhouse on the better milk-producing farm. Today this type of dairy, too, is obsolete, replaced in the last 20 years by the bulk tank system(26).

The Piggery

The piggery is a comparatively recent type of building, as for centuries the domesticated pig, like its wild ancestors, was mainly a woodland animal. The Norman clerks who compiled Domesday Book assessed the value of woodlands in terms of the number of pigs they could support, and mediaeval pigs spent much of the year under the supervision of the village swineherd in the forests, where they foraged on beechnuts and acorns, grubs and carrion. It was only in the succeeding centuries that the conversion of the ancient forests and scrub to farmland gradually compelled farmers to house their pigs along with their other stock on their own land. The change was slow but in most areas it was completed by the eighteenth century, although in Cheshire pigsties were regarded as an innovation as late as the early nineteenth century. It is probably significant that a survey of farm buildings in Staffordshire found no pigsties older than the mid-eighteenth century.

Sometimes pigs were housed in yards, but more commonly they lived in some version of the familiar cottager's pigsty which provides an open run and a shelter, a type of building peculiarly suitable for the pig which, being hairless, is more susceptible to climate than other farm animals.

On dairy farms where pigs were fattened on the by-products of butter-making and cheese-making there were rows of such sties. On other farms, there were often one or two sties near the farmhouse where the farmer's wife could conveniently feed them on household wastes and fatten them for the farmhouse table. In the villages, too, many cottagers kept a pig in a sty in the back garden. This was, indeed, their main source of meat and the pig was an important member of the community. Readers of *Lark Rise to Candleford* will remember Flora Thompson's description of the family pig as 'everybody's pride and everybody's business'.

Today such sties are obsolete. On farms they are far too expensive in labour and have long been replaced by more intensive large-scale systems of housing. In the villages their numbers fell as sanitary standards improved. But a number of derelict sties remain as relics of the time when butter and cheese were made on farms and the countryman fattened, killed and ate his own pork and bacon(27).

Poultry Housing

Traditionally, poultry were no more than a casual sideline of the mixed farming system, by custom the responsibility of the farmer's wife who relied on the sale of eggs for pin-money. They were usually either housed in coops near the farmhouse, where she could feed them conveniently on household waste, or left to find their own homes among the farm buildings, thus leaving no structural relics. Some, however, were kept in lofts or rooms, examples of which dating from the eighteenth and nineteenth centuries were found in a survey of farmsteads in Staffordshire. A unique survival, a late eighteenth century egg production building at Lowick Highstead Farm in Northumberland, recalls more intensive systems and a forgotten but once flourishing local trade which in the time of George III exported eggs by the hundred thousand to London via Berwick-on-Tweed. After the end of the Napoleonic Wars, however, London found it cheaper to obtain supplies from Ireland and the Continent, and the Northumberland farmers turned to other enterprises. The building remains as a useful reminder that there is nothing new in either specialized livestock buildings or overseas competition(28).

The Stable

Until the coming of the tractor, the stable housed the animal teams on which the farmer depended for the cultivation of his land and the haulage of his crops. Today, of course, we associate stables with horses. But for many centuries they housed oxen, for it was only in Victorian times that the horned plough-teams were finally replaced by horses.

Draught oxen have left few traces in the farmstead. Some, it seems, were kept in cowsheds and therefore did not need special buildings and no stables specifically built for oxen have survived, although a section of a longhouse later used for draught oxen can be seen at Castle Farm Folk

Museum, near Bath. Probably the change from oxen to horses often meant no more than different animals in the same stable. In Monmouthshire, however, the memory of the oxen is occasionally preserved by the wide doors made necessary by the great spread of the horns of the local breed. In North Wales the lofts over stables where the horseman slept continue, it is suggested, the mediaeval tradition of the oxherd sleeping with his charges(29).

The few surviving stables for working horses, or for the 'nag' which the farmer rode or drove, give little idea of the importance of the horse in the old agriculture. Traditionally, one horse to 30 acres of ploughland was a common rule-of-thumb and a lifetime ago there was stabling for a million horses on the farms of England and Wales. Today most of them have been demolished or converted, often beyond the point of recognition, to other purposes. Sufficient remain, however, to illustrate the arguments in Hanoverian and Victorian agricultural literature on the sloped floor, ventilation and the advantages and disadvantages of lofts, while occasional recesses in walls for candles recall the winter hours when the horseman fed and groomed his charges in the dark(30).

Sheep Buildings

The sheep has always been the most outdoor of farm animals, but it has long required certain forms of structure. The most ancient of these are the occasional 'buchts' of Northumberland, the remains of small rectangular enclosures where ewes were collected for milking, which preserve the memory of the sheep as a dairy animal. The huge stone sheepfolds characteristic of Snowdonia, but also found elsewhere in Wales, record a more recent period in the economic history of the sheep. They date from the eighteenth century, when the expansion of the Welsh weaving trade meant an increase in the number of sheep, and England offered the only outlet for aged or surplus stock. Now long derelict, these systems of collecting walls, central enclosures and small pens enabled farmers whose sheep grazed the communal uplands to separate their flocks when the time came for the drovers to assemble their drafts for the journey to the English markets(31).

Other pastoral relics are the stone pens in the corners of upland fields, where sheep were gathered for shearing or for foot-paring, the circular stone stells on the hills where they took shelter in hard weather, and the washes in streams through which they were herded to clean their fleeces from dirt and from the homemade salves of tar and butter used to destroy parasites. The old pens and stells are still used, but sheep are no longer washed, because dipping in insecticide is compulsory and the additional price for the washed wool does not cover the cost of the operation. There

has been little systematic study of the structural remains of the older
sheep farming, but a survey of sheep washes in the Peak District found
that almost every village once had its own wash and listed examples of the
pen systems which controlled the movement of the flock. This was
probably one of the last areas to continue the washing of sheep, which in
one parish survived into the 1960s(32).

In fact, the development of sheep housing, which began in the 1960s as
part of the general intensification of farming, revived part of an old
tradition. Nothing is now left of the mediaeval shearing houses and the
dairies where ewes' milk was made into cheese or of the Tudor and Stuart
sheepcotes. It is, however, possible that certain stone houses used for
wintering sheep in the Lake District date from the eighteenth century
and there may be other survivals in other hill areas where this exceptional
practice is traditional(33).

The Dovecote

Nowadays we do not regard pigeons as a form of farm stock. But in the
past their agricultural importance was considerable, for they provided
fresh meat and eggs to vary the limited diet of the period and also left
valuable residues for the dunghill. In early Stuart times, before nitre was
imported from the East Indies, they were also for a brief period a valuable
source of an industrial raw material – saltpetre for gunpowder
manufacture was extracted from the soil of their houses. In feudal times,
however, these benefits were the monopoly of the lord of the manor who
alone could build dovecotes and did not abandon this privilege until the
early seventeenth century.

The massive stone cotes of the Normans which so substantially
symbolized this privilege were later replaced by lighter, more ornamental
buildings, of which examples can be seen at the Avoncroft Museum of
Buildings. The general design, however, altered little. Dovecotes remained
roofed walls thick enough to contain rows of nesting holes which could be
reached by ladder or from a wooden frame revolving round a central
stanchion. From these cotes fluttered the hundreds of birds – 500-600 was
a common size of flock – whose depredations are remembered in the old
agricultural proverb of the four seeds:

> One for the pigeon, one for the crow,
> One to rot and one to grow.

The order is significant.

The new fodder crops introduced in the Agricultural Revolution
which so greatly increased the supply of meat ended the economic
importance of the pigeon, and the men of George III's time emphasized

the harm they did to crops rather than the value of the food and manure they produced. Some farmers, however, continued to built lofts in their barns or cartsheds and as late as the 1880s pigeons still played 'a quite appreciable part in the economy of most farms' in Nottinghamshire. But it is now a long time since domesticated pigeons have contributed more than pleasure and interest to the countryside(34).

The Oasthouse

Hops were first cultivated in this country in Tudor times and with the hop garden came, inevitably, the oasthouse for drying the crop. But the early oasthouses, small barnlike buildings in which the hops were unloaded at one end, dried in a central kiln and carted away from the other end, were very different from those which we now associate with the Kentish landscape. The familiar circular oast topped by a pivoted timber cowl with a flyboard to keep the back of the cowl to the wind was only invented in the 1790s by John Read of Horsmonden, an ingenious gardener who also developed a garden syringe, a stomach pump and a steam heating system for glasshouses. The new type of oasthouse did not become an established feature of the hop-growing countryside until the early nineteenth century and did not replace the older model until half a century later. Occasional examples of the older type, including one probably dating from the seventeenth century, could be seen in Kent 20 years ago and some may survive to this day. Externally, they looked like conventional barns, but the cowls at the kiln tops protruding through the roof ridges showed their real purpose.

The nineteenth century circular oasts, in which hops were moved by men shovelling them, were followed in the early twentieth century by square oasts designed to allow the hops to be moved on horsehair cloth mounted on rollers. The next generation, however, brought more drastic change. Farmers continued to use such oasts but ceased to build them, for electric fans, oil firing and roof louvres have now combined to produce a more efficient though less picturesque type of drying installation. So the mechanization of hop-drying has rendered obsolete the traditional oasthouse, even as the mechanization of hop harvesting has rendered obsolete the traditional annual migration of hop-pickers from London's East End. A survey of some 650 oasthouses in Kent in 1956 found that less than half were still in use for hop-drying. Today the proportion would be very much smaller. Some of the abandoned oasts have been demolished, but a number have been converted to dwelling-houses and so continue to provide the hop-growing landscape with one of its most characteristic features(35).

Building Materials and Methods

Until the early nineteenth century farmers built their farmsteads from such materials as local nature happened to provide. As it was in the days of the Heptarchy, so it was in the days of George III, when the publications of the agricultural improvers gave detailed advice on the planning of farmsteads but not on their construction, because their authors knew that their readers could only use such materials as were available near their farms.

These materials were varied and numerous, timber from the woods, clay from village pits, hazel rods from coppices for wattle-and-daub walling, straw from the fields, reeds from the marshes and ling from the moors for thatch. But the only enduring material available was stone, laborious and expensive to quarry, transport and cut, and consequently for many centuries only used by the wealthy for their buildings, although humbler steadings sometimes stood on stone wall-footings. Most early buildings, therefore, have returned to the soil whence they came, and it is no accident that so many 'tithe barns' are concentrated within the areas of good building stone within a radius of some 75 miles of Bristol. Thus the structural legacy of the Middle Ages is small, but it includes examples of two basic types of timber framework constructions.

The first is the primitive 'cruck' system of pairs of long, heavy timbers, formed by splitting the trunks of curved trees down the middle, roughly squaring them, and setting them opposite each other either in the earth or on a stone base to make the arches which formed the skeleton of the building. Survivals of cruck farm buildings are few, though this method of construction was probably used for many barns and larger livestock buildings on the farms of the more substantial peasantry. There is, indeed, a suggestion that the spacing of approximately 16 feet between crucks often found in various types of building in and after the Middle Ages may have originated in cattle sheds, since a bay of this width holds two pairs of oxen conveniently. The belief is reasonable and, if true, implies the common use of this system of building in mediaeval farmsteads. From Tudor times onwards, however, it was gradually replaced by more advanced types of construction, although a derivative called the 'upper cruck', in which crucks were seated in the ends of first floor beams to form trusses, was used in some Worcestershire farm buildings as late as the second half of the eighteenth century. The sixteenth century Stryt Lydan barn at the Welsh Folk Museum and the sixteenth or seventeenth century Cholstrey barn at the Avoncroft Museum of Buildings are good examples of late cruck construction(36).

The second basic type of timber construction is the more familiar and more sophisticated post-and-truss, or framed construction of upright posts supporting roof trusses, which makes possible aisled buildings. This avoids the restrictions on the height and width of buildings imposed by the cruck system and made possible the cathedral-like splendour of many of the 'tithe barns' and their spacious successors. Such buildings are monuments to the skill of the carpenters who made and jointed the framework with evolving techniques which provide a means of dating these huge structures. The barn at Siddington in Gloucestershire, for example, has been dated by a study of its timberwork to the thirteenth century. Similarly, changing constructional methods used in the Abbot's Hall Barn, now at the Museum of East Anglian Rural Life, show that it was begun in the thirteenth century but also includes timber knees fixed by iron bolts with threaded nuts of a design first used by Wren in 1710(37). This system of framed construction continued the traditions of the Saxon nobleman's hall and was later revived in other materials, first by the Dutch barn and then, in our own generation, by the clad frames of reinforced concrete, steel or treated timber which have increasingly replaced buildings that carry their roofs on weight-bearing walls.

From Tudor times onwards, farm buildings shared in the general tendency towards more spacious design and more durable materials. On the one hand, in the sixteenth century the ancient regional distinction between the cruck barns of the west and the framed barns of the east continued, although the latter were literally gaining ground and super-seding their rivals in the East Midlands. On the other, in the more prosperous areas, there was increasing use of brick, tiles and stone instead of perishable timber, wattle-and-daub and thatch, all of which reflected growing wealth as well as shrinking woodlands. Thus, in Elizabethan and early Stuart times, brick was increasingly used for barns in the prosperous arable areas of south-east England, and one of the first farmsteads in Britain built largely of brick, certainly the first in Wales, dating from 1567, still stands at Bachegraig, Tremeirchion, in Flintshire(38).

Nevertheless, there was no break with the tradition of local self-sufficiency. The stone came from local quarries, the bricks and tiles were made of clay from local pits fired in local kilns. The Tudor craftsman who made the hurdles which wall Stryt Lydan barn, now at the Welsh Folk Museum, worked in the same tradition as 'W. Spears 1805', who wrote and dated his name on a ridge tile made in the estate kiln for a barn at Salisbury Hall, near St Albans. So did the unknown Wiltshire farmer who used the tough stems of old man's beard to bind the wheat thatch of the roof of the adapted longhouse now at Castle Farm Folk Museum, near Bath. The half-timbered, stone, brick and clay-walled barns of different areas of Wales are merely instances of the continuation of regional materials and building methods.

Each area has its own history of change and development. Thus, in the early nineteenth century a new type of building appeared on many farms, but those who built them used the familiar old materials. In Devon they built these wheelhouses with granite pillars, in Norfolk with wooden uprights or flint, in Berkshire with weatherboarding, in the East Riding with brick, in the West Riding with sandstone, in Bedfordshire with ironstone, in Sussex they roofed them with thatch, in the North Riding with pantiles, in Northumberland with stone tiles(39).

The days of the old order, however, were numbered. The great change which was to divide the construction of farm buildings into two distinct traditions began at the end of the eighteenth century, when contemporaries noted the increasing use of slates as the new canals carried them into unfamiliar areas. In the next century, the combination of factory and railway were to complete what the combination of quarry and canal began.

The first consequence of this change was the widespread use of the more enduring traditional materials. Bricks, tiles and slates were now available anywhere in the country and by mid-Victorian times slates were becoming the normal roofing in areas as different as Devon and Northumberland, while Staffordshire landowners were building their farmsteads in brick because it was cheaper than the local stone. The days when farm buildings appeared to grow out of the soil were passing. From this time onwards the materials of which they were built had no necessary connection with the area in which they stood.

A second consequence was the appearance of materials created or developed by the factory system. Glazed windows became normal fittings in farm buildings in early Victorian times and were soon followed by two basic resources of the future, galvanized iron sheeting and concrete. The former quickly established itself as a recognized form of roofing, appreciated for its low cost and for its lightness which made it particularly suitable for replacing decayed thatch on old timber buildings. The latter was only used in its mass form and generally for foundations, although occasionally for above-ground work. It is unlikely that any nineteenth century galvanized iron survives, but the first concrete farm building in the country, a highly exceptional fattening shed erected near Faringdon, in Oxfordshire, by a highly exceptional estate-owner about 1870, still stands, while concrete walls built between 1873 and 1883 can be seen in some of the farmsteads of the Holkham estate in Norfolk(40).

Some of the other mid-Victorian factory products which can still be found in some older farmsteads, such as metal heelposts, metal stall divisions and metal mangers, were new forms of traditional fittings. Some, such as ventilation louvres and rails and rollers for sliding doors, were new devices from the technical world beyond the village workshop. Some, such as cast iron pillars and the iron trusses which bridged wide spans more economically than timber, were structural parts which foreshadowed prefabrication systems to come. Some, more novel, offered new ways of doing old jobs. There was no precedent on the farm for that peculiarly appropriate development of the railway age, the iron tramway for the trollies which carried stacks to the thrashing machines or fodder to the troughs of housed cattle, which are occasionally visible, long abandoned and choked with dirt, in the flooring of once advanced farmsteads.

By the early twentieth century the old tradition of local self-sufficiency passed reluctantly into history. In Norfolk the time-honoured 'clay lump' was used into the early 1900s, in Wiltshire the last use of sarsen stone in a farm building was as late as 1923, local timber continued to be widely used for such rough work as shelters, and in the remoter parts of Wales it was the lorry, not the railway, which enabled factory-made bricks to replace local materials. Nevertheless, the age of the manufacturer and the merchant had come. It was typical of the change that archaeologists recording two surviving cruck barns in Leicestershire in 1954 found that one was roofed with corrugated iron sheeting, a nineteenth century invention, and the other with asbestos-cement sheeting, a twentieth century invention(41).

In general, the materials and methods used in the construction of farm buildings were presumably the same as those used for humbler buildings elsewhere in the locality. But there is one ingrained agricultural tradition of which farm buildings provide occasional interesting evidence. This is the do-it-yourself habit of using any secondhand material that happens to be available, which goes back at least to the thirteenth century, when the monks of Buckfastleigh Abbey built the walls of an upland steading from boulders taken from a nearby Bronze Age settlement, and continues cheerfully to this day(42).

Thus, some of the stones of eighteenth century farm buildings at Rudchester in Northumberland were plundered from Hadrian's wall; the hexagonal ashlar pillars of certain Durham wheelhouses came from Finchale Abbey; the hewn blocks of Furness Abbey, sometimes with elaborate decoration, appear in farm buildings in the Dalton area; a barn dated 1632 at Toddington in Gloucestershire includes a twelfth century windowframe, presumably from some church; one of the early farmsteads built by the great Coke of Norfolk in the late eighteenth century used flint and masonry from the nearby site of a deserted village; and the stable of a Wiltshire farm contains re-used cruck blades from some vanished building. Indeed, the practice is sufficiently common to increase the already considerable difficulties of dating farm buildings.

There are also the numerous local stories of barns built from the timbers of dismantled ships. Admittedly, the use on farms near harbours or rivers of timbers from old ships seems likely in the post-mediaeval centuries when forests were shrinking and demands for wood growing. The only documented case of a farm building built of ship's timbers, however, is the famous seventeenth century barn near the Quaker meeting house at Old Jordans in Buckinghamshire; although unfortunately there is no truth in the claim that they came from the *Mayflower*. Probably most of these re-used timbers were taken not from old ships but from old houses or old barns(43).

The Farmstead

Individual types of building and the materials and methods used in their construction illustrate a variety of historical themes. But, of course, each particular building is only part of the whole farmstead. The siting of farmsteads and the manner in which the different buildings are fitted together to form a practical and convenient pattern can provide evidence on the industrial past above and beyond that recorded by the individual buildings which compose it.

The Farmstead Site

The possible reasons for the choice of site for a farmstead are numerous. They include water, soil, shelter, relationship to fields, to neighbours, to roads. But, as shown in the first two chapters, most farms were won by forgotten reclaimers in forgotten centuries and few farmers have left any evidence, except the sites themselves, of the reasons why they chose the particular sites where they founded their farmsteads. The industrial archaeologist can only deduce these reasons by detailed local studies of reclamation and settlement.

There is, however, one general process of siting farmsteads which is for the most part recent historically and well documented. This is the establishment of new farms which followed the enclosure of open fields and common grazings. Under the old system, many lowland farmsteads clustered in the villages from which farmers went out to their daily work on ploughland and pasture. Under the system which replaced it, farmsteads stood among the fields of the consolidated holdings they served. The process is illustrated by a survey of isolated farmsteads and

47 One of the last of the traditional farm cider-presses in the West Country. The circular building which housed such presses was known as the 'pound house' from the action of the press.

48 An early milking machine, invented by William Murchland in 1889.

49 An early nineteenth century dairy. The dairymaid is working a plunger
butterchurn. Behind her stands a cheesepress and on the left a curdbreaker
and a 'keeler' in which butter was washed. Cheese vats in which the curd
was packed for pressing stand on the shelf and various utensils, including a
buttermould, on the table.

50 A Cotswold waggon, which was regarded by some later eighteenth and early nineteenth century agricultural writers as the best of all English waggons.

51 The oldest agricultural steam engine in the world, built in 1812 by Trevithick for a Cornish landowner to drive a thrashing machine. The original boiler was replaced in 1856. The engine is now in the Science Museum.

52 A Victorian steam-hauled moleplough.

53 The first successful steam ploughing system. It was devised by John Fowler in 1858 and consisted of an engine fitted with a haulage drum stationed at one side of a field opposite a self-propelling anchor and pulley on the other side which hauled the plough across the field on a wire rope. This diorama is in the Science Museum.

54 The Ivel tractor, built by Dan Albone of Biggleswade, was the first effective tractor to be marketed. This is the first Ivel ever manufactured. It was built in 1902 and is probably the oldest tractor in the world. It is now in the Science Museum.

55 The landscape in this diorama is English. The tractor is American, one of the Fordsons imported with other American tractors in 1917 and 1918 to meet the wartime need for fieldpower. This diorama is in the Science Museum.

56 A mediaeval longhouse excavated in Cornwall, probably dating from the thirteenth century. The section of the building nearest the camera is the cowhouse. The flat vertical stones near the walls formed mangers. Holes were bored in them to allow tethering.

57 Plan of mediaeval longhouse in 56.

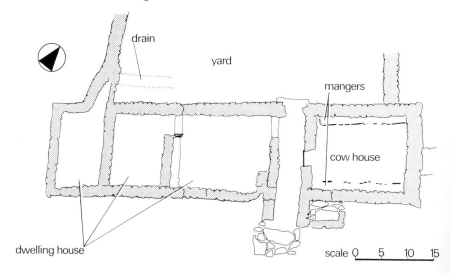

58 A 'Welsh pigsty', possibly the oldest type of farm building now extant. Some 30 buildings of this type survive in Wales.

59 The wheel of an early nineteenth century Northumberland wheelhouse. It was turned by a horse and the power was transmitted by a shaft to the thrashing machine or other machinery in the adjacent barn.

60 A wheelhouse or 'gin-gang' in Northumberland which housed the horse-driven equipment shown in the previous photograph.

61 A Tudor granary presented by the Marquis of Bath to Lackham College of Agriculture, where it was re-erected. The staddle-stones on which it stands provide protection from vermin.

62 Probably the oldest silo in the country. It was built on a Herefordshire farm in 1885, shortly after silage-making was introduced to Britain.

63 A cruck barn in Herefordshire, probably built in the later Middle Ages. A cruck was made of long, heavy timbers from a naturally curving tree which was roughly squared and split in two. The two timbers were then set opposite each other, either in the earth or on a stone base, to make the arches which formed the framework of the building.

64 Internal view of a mediaeval dovecote in Somerset, showing the revolving ladder from which nests could be reached.

65 The interior of a late mediaeval tithe barn in Middlesex. It uses the framed system of construction in which upright posts support roof members to form aisled structures. This made possible considerably larger buildings than the more primitive cruck system.

66 The self-sufficiency of the older agricultural order. The buildings are built of local materials, though the modern age has added corrugated iron sheeting; the farm relies for water on its own pond; and pigeons contribute to the farmer's larder.

67 The first concrete building erected in this country, on the right. This highly unusual cattleshed was built about 1870 of mass-concrete by an enterprising industrialist who owned an estate in Berkshire.

68 (a) and (b)   View and plan of an early eighteenth century Welsh longhouse, which is now in the Welsh Folk Museum, near Cardiff.

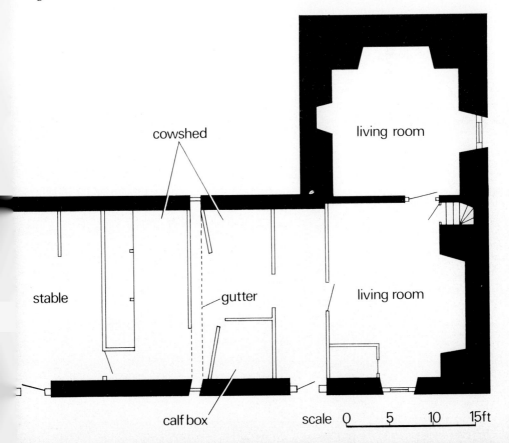

cowshed

living room

stable

gutter

living room

calf box

scale   0   5   10   15ft

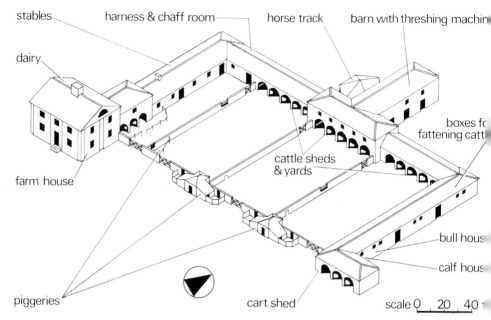

stables · harness & chaff room · horse track · barn with threshing machin[e]

dairy

boxes fo[r]
fattening catt[le]

farm house

cattle sheds
& yards

bull hous[e]

calf hous[e]

piggeries · cart shed · scale 0 20 40 [feet]

69 A farmstead designed for a large farm in 1815, showing the pattern of north range and south-facing yards which was firmly established by this time.

70 A typical early nineteenth century farmstead photographed from the south-west. The corn harvest was stacked north of the buildings and thrashed in the barn. The yard formed by the north range and the two wings of livestock buildings housed cattle which trod straw into manure.

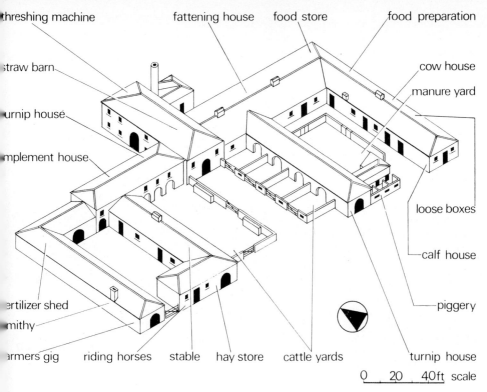

threshing machine   fattening house   food store   food preparation

straw barn

cow house

manure yard

turnip house

implement house

loose boxes

calf house

fertilizer shed

piggery

smithy

farmers gig   riding horses   stable   hay store   cattle yards   turnip house

0   20   40ft scale

71   A farmstead designed in 1849. The corn harvest is thrashed by steam power, but the basic pattern inherited from the Hanoverians continues unchanged.

72   The development of a Berkshire farmstead. The big barn and the flanking livestock buildings round three sides of a south-facing open yard probably date from the time of George III. The buildings with corrugated iron roofing were added in the late nineteenth or early twentieth century, those with asbestos-cement roofing after the Second World War.

73 Part of the north range, including the barn, of a Staffordshire farmstead built in 1863. Here steam power was used for processing feed for livestock which was distributed by trolleys running on a tramway. It also drove a sawmill.

74 A 'haybarn' near Wensleydale. A Board of Agriculture surveyor in 1800 described this area as 'remarkable for its haybarns, which are situated in the centre of every third or fourth field'. Cattle were wintered in them to tread straw into manure for the surrounding fields. So hay and manure were not carried any distance 'an important circumstance in these hilly counties'.

farmsteads in settlements in a lowland area of western Stafford-shire. In 1600, about one farm in six was isolated, in 1775 one farm in three, and by 1880 two in three. Some of these farmsteads were founded on land newly reclaimed from the waste, but the great majority followed the enclosure of open fields and common grazings(44).

The criteria for the siting of farmsteads were first systematically discussed during the period of Parliamentary enclosure in George III's time, when so many new farms were created. But the recommendations of the men of the Agricultural Revolution only recorded immemorial practice. Water inevitably came first, because it was easier to take the farmstead to water than water to the farmstead(45). Shelter, a general need of all farmsteads and a particular need of farmsteads standing in the treeless wastes of former open fields or common grazings, came next and led to the common practice of planting trees round the homestead. The third, to use the word of the time, was 'centricity', for there were many reasons why a farmstead should stand in a central position convenient for its fields, few why it should stand near a road. The farmer was concerned every day with work in the fields, only occasionally with the sale of products off the farm, and a few hundred yards of farm track made little difference to the lumbering waggons or the plodding oxen on their way to market. The days when he would sell milk off his farm every day and receive so many of the necessities of his trade from the road which linked him to factory and port were far ahead. The importance attached to these three factors is obvious to any visitor to the farming countryside.

The application of these general principles can be followed in the establishment of the farmsteads which were built to serve the new farms created by the long processes of enclosure. These enclosures, however, were often gradual and piecemeal and their effects were neither immediate nor complete. Some new farms could be worked conveniently from the old homesteads. Some landlords and farmers only built new farmsteads in their fields when the old ones in the village were no longer worth repairing. Some persisted in building new farmsteads in the villages. Nevertheless, on the whole, as the years passed, a new pattern emerged over much of the lowlands. In the countryside the new buildings slowly mellowed into the landscape until they looked as if they had been there all the time. In the villages many of the old farmhouses became cottages and the old barns and yards were converted into outhouses or allowed to decay. A few of these old farm buildings still survive, the last structural relics of a farming system which has now passed into history(46).

These generalizations can be illustrated by examples chosen almost at random from the considerable mass of historical material on the subject. In Holderness, for example, isolated farmsteads nearly all date from between 1750 and 1850, the earlier ones being in the villages. At Pytchley in Northamptonshire, which was enclosed by agreement, there were no outlying farmsteads in 1779, but by 1817 two had been built and one was under construction. At Theddingworth in Leicestershire, Lodge Farm, which stands outside the village, was built after the enclosure of the parish in the time of Charles I. At Wymesfold, also in Leicestershire, the process was more complicated. After enclosure in 1766 a string of eight new farmsteads was built along the edge of the old north and east open fields. The south field, however, was divided among farmers who continued to work their new land from their old steadings in the village and built only outlying sheds and barns there. Naturally, the consequence of enclosure varied with time and place. Thus, at Wold Newton in Yorkshire, which was enclosed in 1776, three new isolated farmsteads were built in 1776 and two more by 1850, but six farms were still worked from farmsteads in the village. Again, Great Gidding in Huntingdonshire was enclosed during the agricultural depression of the late nineteenth century when few landowners or farmers could afford to build new steadings in their new fields. So Great Gidding has only three farms lying outside the village, whereas the neighbouring parish of Glatton, which was enclosed in more prosperous times, has six. Nevertheless, the general effect of the enclosures is summarized by a comment on the parish of Elford in Staffordshire, enclosed in 1766, where the buildings in the fields are of Georgian and Victorian brick, the buildings in the core of the village of the older half-timbered construction(47).

Sometimes the names of the new farms record their origins. The most obvious examples of this are the various Waterloo Farms, while Leicestershire contains a Quebec, a Belle Isle, a Hanover and a Moscow Farm, as well as the less auspicious New York Farm and Bunkers Hill Farm, the Mendips have a Wellington, a Victoria and an Upper Canada Farm, and the Brecklands a St Helena Farm. Such names as Down, Warren or Newbarn Farm recall the reclamation of the upland grazings which was such a feature of later Hanoverian times and, no doubt, local studies could add many other significant names to the historical list(48).

The Longhouse Tradition

The tradition of erecting varied buildings under one roof has obvious advantages in the economy of materials as well as in shelter, and it survived in the North of England and less frequently elsewhere after the longhouse had been abandoned.

When the farmer and his family had withdrawn to a house separate from the farm buildings, the principle of different functions in one structure continued to be applied to purely agricultural buildings. One example of this is the Pennine barn, some examples of which housed hay on a floor above cattle, others hay and cattle, grain and a thrashing floor under one roof, as can be seen in the seventeenth century barn at the West Yorkshire Folk Museum.

Another example of the same principle is the bank barn, a two-storey building built into a hillside which allows ground-level entry to each storey and convenient storage on the upper floor of hay which is dropped through trapdoors to cattle on the lower floor. At least 400 such barns are known in the Lake District. Most of them, it seems, were built in the nineteenth century, although the oldest date from the early eighteenth or possibly late seventeenth centuries and the most recent from 1904(49).

It is possible, too, that the longhouse tradition lingers in the linear pattern of some early farmsteads where the buildings stand in a straight line. The linear farmsteads of Northumberland, for example, such as the impressive seventeenth century Whiteley Shield Farm high on the uplands above the West Allen, may have developed by a natural and literal extension of the older system. It is perhaps significant, too, that a recent survey of 257 farmsteads in Staffordshire found that this pattern was the earliest classifiable type of layout. As yet, however, there is not enough evidence to allow generalizations on early farmstead plans(50).

Hanoverian Plan and Victorian Development

In 1814 R.W. Dickson, a surveyor of the Board of Agriculture, contrasted the casual chaos of old farmsteads apparently 'built at random, without order or method, whose buildings had accumulated over the generations', with the planned and purposeful layouts of his own time(51). Today the systematic plans of many of the farmsteads originally designed by his contemporaries are equally obscured by additions and alterations, for the process of 'accumulation' did not stop with the Agricultural Revolution. The historical moral is clear. Farming needs change more quickly than farmsteads and, since comprehensive remodelling is seldom practicable, farmers have generally contented themselves with adaptations, additions and piecemeal improvements. Farmsteads may be designed as units. They are seldom modernized as units. Most of the farmsteads we see today, therefore, are the aggregate result of the work of different men meeting different needs at different times with different resources. It is this that gives them their especial value as records of historical change(52).

Dickson's comment, however, also contains another important historical truth. For many centuries farmers had planned and altered their farmsteads according to particular needs and local traditions. But his generation was the first to develop general principles of farmstead design, publish and discuss them in a substantial technical literature, and apply them consciously and systematically.

This change reflected a major rural change, for by this time the varied tenures of earlier periods had hardened into the familiar landlord-and-tenant system under which the landlord, in return for a cash rent, provided the land and its fixed equipment which the tenant-farmer stocked and worked. So responsibility for farm buildings became the prerogative of the leaders of the Agricultural Revolution, the landed gentry and the rising class of professional men which served them as advisors and managers, who usually designed them in their estate offices and built, maintained and adapted them with the staffs of their estate yards or through local contractors(53). Indeed, the planning and construction of farm buildings was one of the major preoccupations of these men and a constant theme in the numerous books and pamphlets which they produced. By the end of the eighteenth century this educated and energetic class, faced with the general need for bigger and better farmsteads created by agricultural improvement and the particular need for new farmsteads created by the Parliamentary enclosures, evolved a highly standardized and effective type of farmstead design which, with a multitude of variations and modifications, was generally adopted throughout the country.

This standard-pattern farmstead was designed to meet the needs of the farmer who both grew crops and kept stock in the mixed farming system which was predominant in most of the country. On the one hand, it provided accommodation for his corn crops and the means of accumulating the manure which maintained the fertility of the fields that grew them. On the other, it provided convenient housing for varied livestock.

Essentially, this type of farmstead consisted of three parts. The first was the barn in which corn from the stackyard was thrashed and from which straw was distributed. The second was the collection of livestock buildings, including buildings for workbeasts, in which straw and hay were trodden or eaten into manure. The third was the strawbedded open yard formed by the barn and the livestock buildings where stock exercised in winter and manure accumulated. The buildings stood around the open yard, sometimes in a square but usually on three sides of a square, some with one yard forming a U-pattern, some with two yards forming an E-pattern. The functional relationship of these component parts was described with classic brevity in a Board of Agriculture publication of 1796. 'The fodder consumed on the farm goes progressively forward from the barnyard through the cattle to the dunghill, without the unnecessary labour generally occasioned by carrying it backwards and forwards', while the hay stacked behind the cattlebuildings 'followed the same progressive course to the dunghill'(54). Then, in due course, the dung was carted to the fields to grow the corn which returned to the barn and so continued the cycle of farmstead operations.

Little is known about the origins of this system. Presumably it was derived from such early systems as the farmsteads known from archaeological evidence to have been built around yards by some of the wealthier peasantry of the Middle Ages in apparent imitation of the courtyards of their lords' manor-houses, or the two rows of buildings facing each other across a yard found on some Welsh farms(55). But it appeared in developed form in the middle of the eighteenth century and seems, with hindsight, to be the most obvious and sensible method of meeting the agricultural needs for which it was designed(56). It was so quickly and widely accepted that it soon became common practice and it was continued in the next century by the Victorians. Its long and successful life proves its efficiency and illustrates the collective technical competence of the men who originated it. To this day, many farmsteads bear the mark of the formal plan originated by the men of George III's time.

In this plan, the yards faced south to catch the sun and avoid at least some of the rain-bearing south-west winds. They were sheltered on the north by the largest building on the farm, the barn – on larger farms, two or even three barns, ideally one for each type of grain – along which stood the north-facing sheds for carts and implements whose timber required protection from sun and rain alike. Into these barns from the rickyard on the north of them came corn for thrashing and winnowing, out of them grain to be stored either in a free-standing granary or in a loft over the cartshed. Out of them, too, came straw for littering the livestock buildings and, above all, the yards.

From this north range, and at right angles to it, ran the wings which formed the yards and contained a medley of buildings, some for storage but most of them for livestock, preferably arranged in accordance with the need for straw. Fattening cattle were housed nearest the barn, then young cattle, and finally cows, working oxen and horses, the last in stables commonly facing east to catch the light of the early morning sun. Pigs, housed in the familiar pen-and-run sties, lived near the farmhouse because they depended on dairy and household by-products. So did poultry which were generally fed by the farmer's wife. Near the cattleyards, sometimes in stacks, sometimes in a barn, stood the haystore. The farmhouse, which on dairy farms contained the rooms where the farmer's wife and daughters processed liquid milk into butter and cheese, usually stood to the south of the steading and allowed the farmer a good supervisory view of the buildings and the work in and around them. The farming system of

the improvers demanded a high standard of management and the farmer
lived at its operational centre, the farmstead.

In its combination of crop and livestock buildings the farmstead
proclaimed the nature of the farming system it served. It also proclaimed
the priorities of the system. The main contemporary criteria of farmstead
design were convenience of arrangement for routine chores, particularly
the feeding, littering and mucking-out of livestock, and the effective
accumulation of manure. But throughout the Hanoverian and Victorian
periods labour was plentiful and cheap, whereas the demands for the
means of fertility were insatiable. Consequently the importance of the
yard as a manure-factory took precedence and forms a pervading theme in
the practice and literature of the time.

In addition, there were a miscellany of minor buildings, some of them
semi-domestic, such as the nag stable for the farmer's riding horse,
housing for his gig, a cider-press in apple-growing areas, and sometimes a
forge or a slaughterhouse. Most of these have now gone, but occasional
survivals recall the days of bad roads, slow transport and consequent
local self-sufficiency.

There were, of course, an infinity of variations to meet local needs,
local circumstances and different sizes and types of farm. But the general
pattern of north range and south-facing yards was universally familiar and
accepted, at least in the lowlands. The hypothetical farmsteads recommended and the new farmsteads illustrated in the publications of the late
eighteenth and of the nineteenth centuries are virtually interchangeable,
and the strength of the tradition thus formalized survives into our own
day. Shortly after the Second World War, an assessment of farm
buildings started with the assumption that 'the ordinary farm building
layout in England is generally three or four sides of a quadrangle with
offshoots'(57). Since then much has changed in the farmstead. But you
cannot go far in most of today's countryside without seeing something of
the work of the Hanoverian and Victorian designers. Indeed, the hiker
can often orient himself by the position of the barn in the farmsteads he
passes.

Nevertheless, there are important differences between the farmsteads
of the Hanoverians and those of the Victorians. The first reflects
constructional change. The Hanoverians were dependent on local
materials, the Victorians could use the products of other areas and new
industries. The second reflects technical change, the use of steampower
with all its implications for design and construction. The third reflects
agricultural change, bigger yards and provision for roofing them to meet
the needs of more and better cattle and to protect the manure. The fourth
is more general and more subtle. The Victorians were consciously men of

the steam age, consciously applying the principles of the factory to the processes of agriculture. The contemporary hopes of repeating in agriculture the steam-driven triumphs of the Industrial Revolution were not fulfilled and the steam-engine did no more than influence the design of the more substantial farmsteads. But the skills of the engineer are as manifest in their farmsteads as the confidence and wealth of the landowners at whose cost they were built.

So it is Victorian farmsteads which attract most attention. Indeed, many of them reflect the power and pride of the Victorian landowners even as the tithe barns reflect the power and pride of the mediaeval church. For the most impressive of these massive and carefully-planned steadings date from the sunlit decades of the mid-nineteenth century, 'the golden age of British farming', when rents and prices, standards and hopes were alike high and visitors from overseas marvelled at the production and prosperity of the English countryside. Only the men of the High Farming, as it was rightly called, would have planned and built such massive steadings as Eastwood Manor Farm at East Harptree in Somerset, which has recently received an official grant as a building of historic importance. Erected in 1858, it provided all the accommodation and services required for the crops and stock of a 900-acre farm, including a combination of water power and steam power in one roofed complex which covers nearly one and a half acres.

Such a steading was, of course, exceptional. But there were others built on similar principles and sometimes on a similar scale, as can be seen in the magnificent contemporary album of illustrated case-studies published by Bailey Denton in 1863 and on the farms of some of the major historical estates to this day. Some of these steadings stood on tenanted land, others on the home farms of improving landowners where they played their part in the practical demonstration of advanced farming methods. The 'model farm' was very typical of this period.

Nevertheless, the Victorians were inheritors as well as innovators, for, as can be seen very clearly in the North of England Open Air Museum at Beamish, their farmsteads were essentially industrialized versions of their predecessors. Most of the materials and equipment were new, but the basic design was traditional. The nineteenth century farmstead continued the eighteenth century pattern of north range and south-facing yards(58).

Outlying Buildings

Not all farm buildings, however, stand in the central farmstead. On some farms it was preferable to winter cattle in isolated buildings in the fields instead of in the main steading. Essentially these outlying buildings were centres for the accumulation of manure whose produce was spread on the surrounding fields, thus saving the haulage of hay and straw from the fields to the farmstead and back again when it had been converted into manure. Such 'field barns', which are more accurately described as field cattle sheds, were known in many areas, although a number have been demolished since the combination of cheap mechanical transport and purchased fertilizers rendered them obsolete.

One interesting type is the barn and yard found on large chalkland farms, notably in Hampshire and Wiltshire. These units generally date from the conversion of much of the Down sheepwalks to ploughland in Napoleonic times and were built to maintain the fertility of the new cornfields which lay too far from the old farmstead to receive their due return of manure. Some were visited daily by a stockman, some included a cottage, although in the next generation the unwillingness of men to live in such isolated homes, particularly as their children would lose any chance of education, provides agreeable evidence of rising rural standards. Similar buildings, often called by such names as High Barn or Wold Barn, were also erected for similar reasons on the higher and more remote parts of large Yorkshire farms. A number of these field barns still stand on lonely uplands as witnesses to the reclaiming energies of our forefathers in the last age of the moving agricultural frontier.

On the downs and wolds the problem was distance, for these secondary steadings could lie a mile away from the central farmstead. In the Pennines and in parts of Wales the problem was the difficulty of transport on steep slopes. This produced in the Yorkshire Dales as early as the seventeenth century and elsewhere probably usually between the late eighteenth and late nineteenth centuries the small two-storey 'hay-barns' which are so typical of some upland areas in the north. In the Dales, for example, stone 'field houses' dot the landscape, sometimes standing in every third or fourth field. These barns housed inwintered cattle on the ground floor and fodder above them and were sometimes built into slopes so that hay could be loaded into the top storey at ground level(59).

Two Estate Case-Studies

Farm buildings may record any of a variety of general trends and particular and often highly localized developments and decisions. Individual buildings and individual farmsteads can, therefore, provide no more than chance evidence of the past. Since most existing buildings were designed in estate offices and built as part of continuing and frequently well-documented estate management plans, the estate is an obvious unit in which to assess the historical development of groups of farm buildings. Indeed, a review of buildings of particular estates logically follows a review of farmsteads even as a review of farmsteads logically follows a review of the different types of farm building. Two recent studies show the value to the industrial archaeologist of combinations of estate field-surveys and estate records and illustrate the background to farm building development as well as its products(60).

One of these studies concerns Lord Middleton's 12,000 acre Birdsall estate in the East Riding of Yorkshire in the late eighteenth and the nineteenth centuries, the other the 42,000 acre Holkham estate in the days of the famous Coke of Norfolk, later Earl of Leicester, and his son and successor in the same period. The two estates differed considerably in character as well as in size. Birdsall, for instance, included large areas of wold rising to nearly 800 feet above sea-level, whereas Holkham lies as level as the rest of East Anglia. In the development of their farm buildings, however, they had much in common.

Between 1790 and 1860 both estates were pre-occupied with building work, Birdsall providing new farmsteads for new farms reclaimed from wold sheepwalks after late eighteenth century enclosures, Holkham improving existing farms by building new or remodelling old farmsteads. Both used the standard Hanoverian plan as a matter of course. Both built barn-and-yard units, sometimes with cottages, for the remoter areas of large farms to provide manure from inwintered cattle for fields far from the main farmstead. Both, in this period, relied on local building materials, in Yorkshire chalk, stone and locally-made bricks and tiles, in Norfolk chalk, flint, straw for thatch and locally-made bricks and tiles, although Birdsall bought softwood imported from the Baltic, whereas Holkham grew its own timber. This dependence on local resources is interestingly reflected in a feature of the Holkham steadings. There is no stone in Norfolk and therefore no staddle-stones to protect grain from vermin. Consequently, grain was stored over cartsheds and not in separate granaries. And both, like other estates, relied on local technical talent, for buildings were usually designed by the landowner's agent. Coke, however, in the 1780s and 1790s temporarily employed Wyatt the architect who built three farmsteads, one of which remains largely as he left it, as well as the Great Barn where Coke held the agricultural demonstrations he called 'Sheepshearings'. His son, in mid-Victorian times, temporarily employed Dean, one of the most prominent farm architects of his age.

After 1860 each estate built only one new farmstead, though both continued to improve their farmsteads, Birdsall by roofing open yards at the end of the century, Holkham mainly by increasing accommodation

for livestock and building smithies where the village blacksmith on
regular visits could maintain and repair the growing number of iron
implements. The memorials of this century of change still survive, as do
many of the records of their planning, construction and adaptation. At
Birdsall, for instance, 20 of the 24 farmsteads built after the enclosures
followed the standard Hanoverian plan and there were particular local
reasons for the exceptions. The development of one of them, Aldro
Farm, can be followed in some detail on paper and on the site from its
origins to the present. The land was originally an 840-acre sheepwalk
purchased in 1766 and gradually converted to ploughland. In 1772 a map
showed a house and apparently a single range of buildings on the site. By
1810 a single yard farmstead had been built, by 1850 it had expanded into
a two range steading capable of serving the needs of a substantial arable
holding, and today the Dutch barns, grain store, sheep buildings and
covered yard of the modern age fit in and around the pattern established
in the days of George III and Victoria. Then, too, the Home Farm, built
in 1868, is a typical example of Victorian work, complete with two roofed
yards and a fodder processing unit possibly at first powered by steam but
after 1875 by a gas engine which still survives.

At Holkham, the magnificent and possibly unique chronological series
of farmsteads includes Waterden Farm, which was praised when new in
1784 by Arthur Young and, little altered, remains one of the best early
examples of the Hanoverian plan. It ends with Egmere Farm, built in
1857, which is one of the culminating triumphs of this tradition. Built by
Dean to serve a farm of 1,222 acres, this farmstead survives almost as completed, even retaining the original thick glass in the windows of some of
the livestock buildings. Its orderly plan, massive structures and carefully
designed fittings, such as cast-iron uprights, cast-iron thresholds, ramps to
doors for wheelbarrows, stockproof latches and wooden lintels continuing
the brick pattern over the doors in an unexpected agricultural *trompe-l'oeil*,
make manifest the resources and attention to detail of the industrial age.

The buildings of the two estates also record changes in the materials
used for farm buildings. Thus, Red House Farm at Birdsall, built in the
time of George III with chalk, stone and local brick, was largely rebuilt in
the 1860s with imported brick, slates and tiles as well as local stone.
Holkham, which was some distance from a railway, continued to use its
own bricks and tiles, although in the late nineteenth century it sometimes
reduced costs by using flints from its own fields. Less traditionally, it
experimented in the 1870s and 1880s with concrete which survives in one
or two buildings and in a massive barn wall on Egmere Farm. The results
were unsatisfactory, and the material was abandoned.

Many of the old buildings on these two estates are physically and technically impressive as well as historically important. But at Birdsall there are also a few survivals from an earlier age, less obvious but equally interesting. These are the remains of the old farmsteads built before the reclamation of the wolds. Originally all the farms in this area huddled in the villages in the valleys while the uplands were virtually uninhabited. But as farmers migrated to the new farmsteads on the wolds, the village farmsteads were gradually abandoned and now only the houses and barns remain. The moral for the industrial archaeologist is clear: behind the survivals of any industrial age lie the survivals of the previous industrial age which it superseded. Much of the fascination of the subject lies in this continuity and there are few places where it can be better seen than in the farming countryside.

References

Chapter 1

1. PENNINGTON, W., *A History of British Vegetation*, 1974, pp.82-3.

2. For examples of such studies see ROBERTS, B.K., A Study of Mediaeval Colonisation in the Forest of Arden, Warwickshire', *Agricultural History Review*, 1968, pp.101-113, and *Farming, Wildlife and Landscape, Essex Exercise*, 1975, published by the Farming and Wildlife Advisory Group, The Lodge, Sandy, Bedfordshire, which traces nine centuries of change in a wooded area near Widdington.

3. SACKVILLE-WEST, V., *The Land*, 1926, p.10.

4. RACKHAM, O., *Trees and Woodlands in the British Landscape*, 1976, p.65.

5. RACKHAM, O., *Trees and Woodlands in the British Landscape*, 1976, p.64.

6. EDLIN, H.L., *The Changing Wildlife of Britain*, 1952, pp.23, 25, 46, 61; FITZGERALD, B.V., *The Vanishing Wildlife of Britain*, 1969, p.83.

7. MUNBY, L.M., *The Suffolk Landscape*, 1968, p.46; TAYLOR, C., *Fields in the English Landscape*, 1975, pp.126-7.

8. POLLARD, E., HOOPER, M.D. and MOORE, N.W., *Hedges*, 1974 pp.30, 33, 87. In the Weald, wide strips of residual woodland called shaws still border many relatively small fields (BRANDON, S., *The Sussex Landscape*, 1974, pp.34, 96).

9. For the importance of woodland plants as historical evidence see POLLARD, E., HOOPER, M.D. and MOORE, N.W., *Hedges*, 1974 pp.86-104.

10. EMERY, F., *The Oxfordshire Landscape*, 1974, p.86.

11. TAYLOR, C., *The Cambridgeshire Landscape*, 1973, pp.85-6, 101. See also RACKHAM, O., *Trees and Woodlands in the British Landscape*, 1976, p.114

12. For the value of placenames in this context see HOSKINS, W.G., *The Making of the English Landscape*, 1955, p.48; RENNELL of RODD, Lord,

Valley on the March, 1958, pp.61–2; MUNBY, L.M., *East Anglian Studies*, 1968, pp.34–6; POCOCK, E.A., 'The First Fields in an Oxfordshire Parish', *Agricultural History Review*, 1968, pp.85–100; FIELD, J., *English Field Names*, 1970; McRAE, S.G. and BURHAM, C.P., *The Rural Landscape of Kent*, 1973, p.160; RAISTRICK, A., *The West Riding of Yorkshire*, 1970, p.54; BRANDON, P., *The Landscape of Sussex*, 1974, pp.27, 72, 77, 83, 86, 99; STEANE, J.M., *The Northamptonshire Landscape*, 1974, pp.68, 73, 98; RACKHAM, O., *Trees and Woodland in the British Landscape*, 1976, pp.55–6. See also the publications of the English Place-Name Society.

13. TAYLOR, C., *The Cambridgeshire Landscape*, 1973, p.99; EMERY, F., *The Oxfordshire Landscape*, 1974, p.81 refers to fieldnames with this element left by mediaeval reclamation in the Ploughley area. As late as 1772 the name of Breachfield was given to an area of Eggbury Down, near St Mary Bourne, first brought under the plough in that year (JONES, E.L., 'Eighteenth Century Changes in Hampshire Chalkland Farming', *Agricultural History Review*, 1960, p.14).

14. HOSKINS, W.G., *Provincial England*, 1963, p.219; GRIGSON, G., 'The Ghost of a Forest', *Country Life*, 24 January, 1957, pp.138–40.

15. WISE, S.E., *What is Wychwood?*, Cocklands Press, Burford, 1974, reference to Langley Farm on p.22. See also EMERY, F., *The Oxfordshire Landscape*, 1974, pp.158–9. Readers of Hearne will remember that on 14 September 1732 Queen Caroline sent the Fellows of Magdalene College a buck from Wychwood. HIGGS, J., *The Land*, 1964, shows in photo 175 the substantial steading of Potter Hill Farm, built in 1858 to serve the fields where this buck once roamed. Another royal forest, Hainault, near Chigwell, whose remnants are familiar to many Londoners, was also disafforested in this period. It was reclaimed in 1851, '92% of it disappearing with a speed which would have done credit to modern bulldozers'. (RACKHAM, O., *Trees and Woodlands in the British Landscape*, 1976, p.154).

16. Information by courtesy of the Rev. R.P. Rankin. For the encroachments on Charnwood Forest and its final enclosure see Victoria County History, *History of the County of Leicestershire*, 1954, vol. 2, pp.268–70.

17. DAVIES, C.D., *The Agricultural History of Cheshire, 1750–1850*, 1960, p.8.

18. HOSKINS, W.G. and FINBERG, H.P.R., *Devonshire Studies*, 1952, p.336; BALCHIN, W.G.Y., *Cornwall*, 1954, p.41; EDWARDS, K.C., SWINNERTON, H.H. and HALL, R.H., *The Peak District*, 1962, p.133; RAISTRICK, , A., *The Pennine Dales*, 1968, pp.115–6.

19. ROBERTS, A., 'The Historical Development of Hill Farming in Wales', *Agricultural Progress*, 1949, p.26 for 1862 summering; MILLWARD, R., *Lancashire*, 1955, pp.14, 29, 31; HOSKINS, W.G., *Common Land, 1955–1958*, 1958, p.153; THIRSK, J., in review of CAMERON, K., *Placenames of Derbyshire*, 1959, in *Agricultural History Review*, 1960, p.120; FINBERG, H.P.R., (ed.), *The Agrarian History of England and Wales, 1500–1640*, 1967,

pp.149–50; ROYAL COMMISSION ON HISTORICAL MONU-MENTS, *Shielings and bastles*, 1970, which lists sites in Cumberland and Northumberland; COWLEY, B., *Farming in Yorkshire*, 1972, p.20; NEWTON, B., *The Northumberland Landscape*, 1972, p.104 for Batail-shieling; PEARSALL, W.H. and PENNINGTON, W., *The Lake District*, 1973, p.244; SMITH, P., *Houses of the Welsh Countryside*, 1975, pp.142–4; WILLIAMS, M., *The South Wales Landscape*, 1975, pp.91–2, 192; DAVIES, E., 'Hendre and Hafod in Denbighshire', *Denbighshire Historical Society Transactions*, 1977, pp.49–72.

20. JOHNSON, A., 'Enclosure and Changing Agricultural Landscapes in Lindsey', *Agricultural History Review*, 1963, p.96.

21. TAYLOR, C., *Dorset*, 1970, pp.133–4.

22. BALCHIN, W.G.V., *Cornwall*, 1954, pp.41–2; HOSKINS, W.G., *English Landscapes*, 1973, p.29. For other examples see FINBERG, H.P.R. (ed.), *The Agrarian History of England and Wales, 1500–1640*, 1967, pp.148–50 and HARRIS, H., *The Industrial History of Dartmoor*, 1968, p.145.

23. NEWTON, R., *The Northumberland Landscape*, 1972, p.35.

24. NEWTON, R., *The Northumberland Landscape*, 1972, pp.119–21; FUSSELL, G.E., 'The Reclamation of the Wolds', *Journal of the Land Agents' Society*, April 1954, pp.159–62; HARRIS, A., *The Rural Landscape of the East Riding of Yorkshire, 1700–1850*, 1961, pp.69–77, 124; CHAPMAN, J., Parliamentary Enclosures in the Uplands. The Case of the North York Moors', *Agricultural History Review*, 1976, pp.1–17.

25. ORWIN, C.S. and SELLICK, R.J., *The Reclamation of Exmoor Forest*, 1970.

26. HARRIS, H., *The Industrial Archaeology of Dartmoor*, 1968, p.204.

27. Two Italian engineers recovered the Combe Marsh near Greenwich in the reign of Henry VIII (SMILES, S., *Lives of the Engineers*, 1862, p.14). But the main source of drainage expertise was Holland. Vanderdelf, who in the same period inned Wapping Marsh, had many successors (ADDISON, W., *Thames estuary*, 1954, pp.154–5). In 1563 the reclamation of Plumstead Marsh was delayed by the difficulty of getting experienced Dutch workmen from the Netherlands (ROWSE, A.L., *The England of Elizabeth*, 1964, p.68) and when Cornelius Vermuyden, the most famous of all Dutch drainers, came to England in 1621, he found a number of his compatriots established here. Vermuyden is, of course, remembered for his achievement in the Fenlands, but he began his career as an assistant to his fellow-countryman, Croppen-burgh, working first on the repair of the Dagenham seawall and later on the embanking of Canvey Island, where part of his wall is now Canvey High Street. In 1626 he undertook the drainage of Hatfield Chase near Doncaster, which included the cutting of the Dutch River from the Don to the Ouse (HARRIS, L.E., *Vermuyden and the Fens*, 1953; CRACKNELL, B.E., *Canvey Island, the History of a Marshland Community*, 1959, pp.17–20, 33;

WAGRET, P., *Polderlands*, 1968, p.90; RAISTRICK, A., *The West Riding of Yorkshire*, 1970, p.83; SMITH, J.R., 'Keeping the sea out of Essex', *Prospect*, published by Redland Purle Ltd., Rayleigh, Essex, Autumn 1975, p.11 which reproduces an early 17th century map of an area in Dagenham 'lately inned by the Dutchmen'). In the 17th century Dutchmen were also employed on the unsuccessful inning of Brading Haven in the Isle of Wight and on the drainage of Whixhall Moss in Maelos Saesneg on the borders of Shropshire and Flint (SMILES, S., *Lives of the Engineers*, 1862, p.135; SYLVESTER, D., *The Rural Landscape of the Welsh Borderland*, 1969, p.52). In Foulness the influence of the Dutch settlers who came in the 17th century to drain and embank was so strong that many women still wore Dutch costume as normal attire in the early 1900s (SMITH, J.R., *Foulness*, 1970, p.42). Two circular cottages dated 1618 and 1621 built by Dutch settlers after the reclamation survive on Canvey Island.

28. *Archaeologia Cantiana*, 1950, p.145; WRIGHT, P.A., *Old farm implements*, 1961, pp.58, 73.

29. HOSKINS, W.G., 'The Road Between', *Listener*, 13 May 1954, p.819.

30. BUCHNER, G.E., 'A reclamation near Wainfleet, Lincolnshire', Institution of Civil Engineers, 1949, summarises the history of Wash reclamations on pp.4–9 and estimates that 38,000 acres were won in the 17th century, 14,000 in the 18th century and 16,000 in the 19th century; DARBY, H.C., *Draining of the Fens*, 1956, p.201, 210; THIRSK, J., *English Peasant Farming*, 1957, pp.17, 132, 219–20; HALLAM, H.E., *Settlement and Society*, 1965; GRIGG, D., *The Agricultural Revolution in South Lincolnshire*, 1966, pp.109, 126; STAMP, L.D., *The Land of Britain*, 1962, p.231, gives a map of innings from 1852 to 1936.

31. TAYLOR, C., *The Cambridgeshire Landscape*, 1973, pp.106–8.

32. HOSKINS, W.G., and FINBERG, H.P.R., *Devonshire Studies*, 1952, pp.118, 319.

33. MAUROIS, A., *Ariel*, 1924, chap. 15; BLUNDEN, E., *Shelley*, 1964, pp.84–5; BEASLEY, A., *Madocks and the Wonder of Wales*, 1967, pp.57–60, 135–68, 192–4, 256.

34. SYLVESTER, D., *The Rural Landscape of the Welsh Borderland*, 1969, pp.70, 396; WILLIAMS, M., *The South Wales Landscape*, 1975, p.105.

35. BRANDON, P., *The Landscape of Sussex*, 1974, pp.111–13.

36. HOSKINS, W.G., *Fieldwork in Local History*, 1967, p.151.

37. HARRIS, A., *The Rural Landscape of the East Riding of Yorkshire, 1750–1850*, 1961, pp.10, 84; ALLISON, K.J., *The East Riding of Yorkshire Landscape*, 1976, pp.134, 171–3.

38. CRACKNELL, B.E., *Canvey Island, the History of a Marshland Community*, 1959, pp.17–20, 33; SMITH, J.R., *Foulness*, 1970, pp.25–32.

39. SMITH, R.A.L., 'Marsh embankment and sea defence in mediaeval Kent',

Economic History Review, February, 1940; HARVEY, N., 'The Inning and Winning of Romney Marsh', *Agriculture*, October 1955, pp.334–8; MURRAY, W.J.C., *Romney Marsh*, 1972, pp.16–40. A map of the innings up to the end of the 17th century prepared 'after consulting the oldest documents with the modern state of affairs circa 1873' by James Elliot, 'sometime engineer of Romney Marsh' is preserved in Stone-cum-Oxney church. Other maps of the innings are given in MURRAY, W.J.C., *Romney Marsh*, 1972, p.17; HARVEY, N., *Ditches, Dykes and Deep Drainage*, 1956, p.13; and McRAE, S.G. and BURNHAM, C.P., *The Rural Landscape of Kent*, 1973, pp.37–9.

40. HALLAM, S.E., *Settlement and Society*, 1965.

41. ESSEX COUNTY COUNCIL, *Essex Landscape No. 1, Historic features*, 1974, pp.23–6.

42. CLARKE, J.A., 'The farming of Lincolnshire', *Journal of the Royal Society of England*, 1851, p.287; STAMP, L.D., *The Land of Britain* pp.76–7, *Lincolnshire (part of Lindsey and Kesteven)*, 1942, pp.489–90; THIRSK, J., *English Peasant Farming*, 1957, pp.230–2, 291; RAISTRICK, A., *The West Riding of Yorkshire*, 1970, pp.83–4; ALLISON, K.J., *The East Riding of Yorkshire Landscape*, 1976, pp.175–6.

43. PARKER, R., *The Common Stream*, 1975, pp.42, 50, 183; SCARFE, N., *The Suffolk Landscape*, 1972, p.88; BELL, A., *The Cherry Tree*, 1941 ed. p.53.

44. TAYLOR, C., *The Cambridgeshire Landscape*, 1973, p.191 with map p.190. The drainage of the Fens has produced the most substantial literature of all area reclamations, notably DARBY, H.C., *The Mediaeval Fenlands*, 1940; ENNION, E.A.R., *Adventurers Fen*, 1949; HARRIS, L.E., *Vermuyden and the Fens*, 1953; ASTBURY, A.K., *The Black Fens*, 1958; DARBY, H.C., *The Drainage of the Fens*, 1956; HALLAM, E., *Settlement and Society*, 1965; HILLS, R.L., *Machines, Mills and Uncountable Costly Necessities*, 1967; MUTTON, H., 'The Use of Steam Drainage in the Making of the Eau Brink Cut', *Industrial Archaeology*, 1967, pp.353–7; TAYLOR, C., *The Cambridgeshire Landscape*, 1973; PARKER, A., and PYE, D., *The Fenlands*, 1976; and SUMMERS, D., *The Great Level*, 1976. THE ROYAL COMMISSON ON HISTORICAL MONUMENTS FOR ENGLAND, *Inventory of Historical Monuments in the County of Cambridgeshire, Vol. 2, North-east Cambridge*, 1972, pp.LIV–LXII, gives a detailed introduction to the Fenland drainage survivals in the area which are listed by parish later in the volume.

45. PARKER, A., and PYE, D., *The Fenlands*, 1976, pp.166–75, summarizes information on these mechanical survivals.

46. The surviving windpump originally stood in Burwell Fen. It now stands in Wicken Fen, which is owned by the National Trust. It was built in 1908 and drained some 30 acres, whereas most of the earlier windpumps were very

much larger and designed to drain up to 500 or 600 acres. TAYLOR, C., *Fenland Pumping Engines*, Cambridge Society for Industrial Archaeology, 1974, pp.2–4.) For windpump sites see HINDE, K.S.G., 'Windpump Remains in the Fens', *Cambridge Industrial Archaeology*, 1973, pp.18–21, who gives the figure of 400 windpumps on p.18; TAYLOR, C., *The Cambridgeshire Landscape*, 1973, pp.201, 205, which includes a reference to Soham Mere where the sites of three windmills operating a treble-lift made necessary by the fall in the level of the surrounding peatland are visible and TAYLOR, C., *Fenland Pumping Engines*, Cambridge Society for Industrial Archaeology, 1974, pp.3–4.

47. The engine at Stretham, which is now owned by the Stretham Engine Preservation Trust and is open to the public, is the largest and the earliest of these. The other two are at Pinchbeck Marsh and Tattersfield. A list, with map references, of 74 sites of engines installed by local drainage boards (but not of engines erected privately by farmers, on which little information is available) is given in HINDE, K.S.G., *Steam in the Fens*, Cambridge Society for Industrial Archaeology, 1974, pp.14–19. Details of remains are included and sites particularly worth visiting noted. For details of engines erected between 1817 and 1835 see HILLS, R.L., *Machines, Mills and Uncountable Costly Necessities*, 1967, pp.157–62.

48. HILLS, R.L., *Machines, Mills and Uncountable Costly Necessities*, 1967, p.iv. The Hundred Foot Engine house stands about two miles east of Manea.

49. CLARKE, C.O., 'The Stretham diesel engine', *Cambridge Industrial Archaeology*, 1973, pp.8–12 gives the history of the engine which replaced the Stretham steam engine in 1924 and ceased work in 1966.

50. TAYLOR, C., *Fenland Pumping Engines*, Cambridge Society for Industrial Archaeology, 1974, p.6. The enginehouse still stands about two miles north east of Holme, Huntingdonshire.

51. ASTBURY, A.K., *The Black Fens*, 1958, p.14; DARBY, H.C., *The Drainage of the Fens*, 1956, p.229.

52. ASTBURY, A.K., *The Black Fens*, 1958, p.44.

53. TAYLOR, C., *The Cambridgeshire Landscape*, 1973, pp.192, 194, 205.

54. ASTBURY, A.K., *The Black Fens*, 1958, p.27; TAYLOR, C., *The Cambridgeshire Landscape*, 1973, pp.29, 204.

55. WAILES, R., *The English Windmill*, 1954, pp.72, 78, 151, 152. See also SMITH, A.C., *Drainage Windmills of the Norfolk Marshes*, published by the Society for the Protection of Ancient Buildings, 1978.

56. SHEPPARD, A.J., *The Drainage of the Hull Valley*, 1958; HARRIS, A., *The Rural Landscape of the East Riding of Yorkshire, 1700–1850*, 1961, pp.47–8; ALLISON, K.J., *The East Riding of Yorkshire Landscape*, 1976, p.77.

57. WILLIAMS, M., *The Draining of the Somerset Levels*, 1970. For the comment on later improvements see KELTING, E.L., *River Boards*

Yearbook, 1958, p.125. For Girard Fossarius see HOSKINS, W.G., *Fieldwork in Local History*, 1967, pp.166–7; for Sedgemoor see WARNER, P., *Fontana British Battlefields, The South*, 1975, pp.122–4.

58. MILLWARD, R., *Lancashire*, pp.43, 52–5. See also HALL, B.R., *Proceedings of North of England Soils Discussion Group*, 1968, p.25. For family memories of the mossland reclamation in Lancashire see J. HOUGHTON, *Countryman*, Summer 1976, pp.118–20.

59. HOSKINS, W.G., *History from the Farm*, 1970, p.129.

60. HOUGHTON, J., *Countryman*, Summer 1976, pp.118–20. The area described is across the Wyre from Fleetwood.

61. STEANE, J.M., *The Northamptonshire Landscape*, 1974, pp.237–8.

62. EMERY, F., *The Oxfordshire Landscape*, 1974 p.156.

63. FINBERG, H.P.R., *The Gloucestershire Landscape*, 1975, p.80.

64. RACKHAM, O., *Trees and Woodlands in the British Countryside*, 1976, p.145.

65. RACKHAM, O., *Trees and Woodlands in the British Countryside*, 1976, p.143.

66. MUNBY, L.M., *The history of King's Langley*, 1963, pp.11, 20, 41, 62. For deerparks and their remains, see WHITAKER, J., *A Description of the Deer Parks and Paddocks in England*, 1892; BALCHIN, W.G.V., *Cornwall*, 1954, p.70; HOSKINS, W.G., *The Making of the English Landscape*, 1955, p.76; HOSKINS, W.G., *Leicestershire*, 1957, p.41; HOSKINS, W.G., *Fieldwork in Local History*, 1967, pp. 51–4 which describes the banks of Marshwood in Dorset as 'rivalling the defensive earthworks of Offa's Dyke'; RAISTRICK, A., *The West Riding of Yorkshire*, 1970, p.53 including references to such placenames as Roebucks, Doestones and Deerstones; TAYLOR, C., *Dorset*, 1970, pp.100, 127, 204; NEWTON, R., *The Northumberland Landscape*, 1972, p.116; ROWLEY, T., *The Landscape of Shropshire*, 1972, pp.167, 120 and on p.122 a map of about 1600 of the clearance of Tirlestock Park showing farmers Gregorie, Greene and Chawnes at work with axes in the areas allocated to them; SCARFE, N., *The Suffolk Landscape*, 1972, p.171; LOVEJOY, D., *Land Use and Landscape Planning*, 1973, p.107; TAYLOR, C., *The Landscape of Cambridgeshire*, 1973, p.130; BRANDON, P., *The Landscape of Sussex,*, 1974, pp.106–7; EMERY, F., *The Oxfordshire Landscape*, 1974, p.91; ESSEX COUNTY COUNCIL, *Essex Landscape No. 1, Historic Features*, 1974, pp.17–18; STEANE, J.M., *The Northampton-shire Landscape*, 1974, pp.175–9, 210, 212, 222; WILLIAMS, M., *The Landscape of South Wales*, 1975, pp.109–10, 142; ALLISON, K.J., *The East Riding of Yorkshire Landscape*, 1976, pp.89–93, 137, 138; PALLISER, D.M., *The Staffordshire Landscape*, 1976, pp.89–91, 108; RACKHAM, O., *Trees and Woodlands in the British Landscape*, 1976, pp.64, 142–51, 163 for Hatfield Forest; TAYLOR, C., *Fields in the British Landscape*, 1976, p.158; MUNBY, L.M., *The Hertfordshire Landscape*, 1977, pp.150–6.

67. PAYNE-GALLWAY, SIR RALPH, *The Book of Duck Decoys*, 1886; WHITAKER, J., *British Duck Decoys of Today*, 1918; DARBY, H.C., *Draining of the Fens*, 1956, pp.88, 92, 157–61, including a plan of a decoy on p.160; WILLIAMS, M., *The Draining of the Somerset Levels*, 1970, p.173; STEANE, J.M., *The Northamptonshire Landscape*, 1974, p.238; ESSEX COUNTY COUNCIL, *Essex Landscape No. 1, Historic Features*, 1974, pp.24–7. Decoys survive at Boarstall, Oxfordshire, Borough Fen, Peakirk, Northamptonshire, Hale, near Liverpool and Slimbridge, Gloucestershire.

68. For warrening see 'Rabbit warrens and their Returns', published in 1878, in *Field and farm. The collected essays of Richard Jefferies*, ed. LOOKER, S.J., 1957, pp.138–40; VEALE, E., 'The rabbit in England', *Agricultural History Review*, 1957, pp.85–90; HARRIS, A., *The rural landscape of the East Riding of Yorkshire*, 1961, pp.78, 97, 101; SHEAIL, J., *Rabbits and their history*, 1971; and SHEAIL, J., 'Changes in the supply of wild rabbits, 1790–1810', *Agricultural History Review*, 1971, pp.175–7. For warrens and their remains see HOSKINS, W.G., *Leicestershire*, 1957, p.54, who refers to Lubbesthorpe Lawn, south of the Leicester-Hinkley road and east of Desford crossroads, the site of a warren first recorded in 1372, which 'cannot have changed at all since the Middle Ages'; LINEHAN, C.D., 'Deserted sites and rabbit warrens on Dartmoor, Devon', *Mediaeval Archaeology*, 1966, pp.113–44; HARRIS, H., *The Industrial Archaeology of Dartmoor*, 1968, pp.154–6 who includes a gazetteer of sites; LONG, W.H., *Survey of the Agriculture of Yorkshire*, 1969, p.29; HAYNES, R.G., 'Vermin Traps and Rabbit Warrens on Dartmoor', *Post-Mediaeval Archaeology*, 1970, pp.147–64, which includes a gazetteer of sites; TAYLOR, C., *Dorset*, 1970, p.133; SHEAIL, J., *Rabbits and their History*, 1971, p.45; BRANDON, P., *The Landscape of Sussex*, 1974, pp.110, 118; ARMSTRONG, P., *The changing Landscape*, 1975, p.79; STEANE, J.M., *The Northamptonshire Landscape*, 1974, pp.179, 205; RACKHAM, O., *Trees and Woodlands in the British Landscape*, 1976, p.163, for the warren in Hatfield Forest, Essex. For warreners' houses see SHEAIL, J., *Rabbits and their History*, 1971, pp.51–2; SCARFE, N., *The Suffolk Landscape*, 1972, p.196; RACKHAM, O., *Trees and Woodlands in the British Landscape*, 1976, p.163.

Chapter Two

1. HOSKINS, W.G., *The Making of the English Landscape*, 1955, p.22; HARRIS, H., *Industrial Archeaology of the Peak District*, 1971, pp.137–8; ROWLEY, T., *The Shropshire Landscape*, 1972, p.34; BAKER, A.R.H. and BUTLIN, R.A., *Studies of Field Systems in the British Isles*, 1973, p.35; BRANDON, P., *The Landscape of Sussex*, 1974, pp.63, 64, 268; FINBERG, H.P.R., *The Gloucestershire Landscape*, 1975, p.37; TAYLOR, C., *Fields in the English Landscape*, 1975, pp.27, 31, 38, 41; WILLIAMS, M., *The*

Landscape of South Wales, 1975, p.87. THE ROYAL COMMISSION ON HISTORICAL MONUMENTS FOR ENGLAND, *Inventory of Historical Monuments for the County of Dorset, Vol. 3, Central Dorset*, Part 2, 1970, pp.318–45, gives a detailed description of the 'Celtic' field groups in this area.

2. TAYLOR, C., *Fields in the English Landscape*, 1975, pp.24, 25. For modern experience with a reconstructed *ard* at the Iron Age Farm project at Butser Hill, Hampshire, see REYNOLDS, P.J., *Farming in the Iron Age*, 1976, pp.6–8.

3. BALCHIN, W.G.V., *Cornwall*, 1954, pp.28, 33, 43, 52; HOSKINS, W.G., *English Landscapes*, 1973, p.42; POLLARD, E., HOOPER, M.D., and MOORE, N.W., *Hedges*, 1974, pp.28–9.

4. BALCHIN, W.G.V., *Cornwall*, 1954, p.45; BERESFORD, M.W. and ST JOSEPH, J.K.S., *Mediaeval England, an Aerial Survey*, 1958, pp.46–9; POLLARD, E., HOOPER, M.D., and MOORE, N.W., *Hedges*, 1974, p.30.

5. POSTGATE, M.R., 'The Field System of Breckland', *Agricultural History Review*, 1960, p.96. The age of the system in this area is, however, uncertain(p.90).

6. STEANE, J.M., *The Northamptonshire Landscape*, 1974, p.108.

7. TAYLOR, C., *The Cambridgeshire Landscape*, 1973, p.83; TAYLOR, C., *Fields in the English Landscape*, 1975, p.96; TAYLOR, C., *Dorset*, 1970, pp.107–8.

8. SCARFE, N., *The Suffolk Landscape*, 1972, pp.218–9.

9. JENKINS, J.G.,*Life and Tradition in Rural Wales*, 1976, p.14

10. HOSKINS, W.G., *Fieldwork in Local History*, 1967, pp.18, 45, 128.

11. For a discussion of current views on the origins of the open field system see BAKER, A.R.H. and BUTLIN, R.A., *Studies of Field Systems in the British Isles*, 1973, pp.622–44, 655–66 and TAYLOR, C., *Fields in the English Landscape*, 1975, pp.68–77.

12. For a general account of the system see AULT, W.O., *Open Field Farming in Mediaeval England*, 1972.

13. For case studies of the processes of enclosure see BERESFORD, M.W. and ST JOSEPH, J.K.S., *Mediaeval England, an Aerial Survey*, 1958, pp.25–40. For a bibliography of this substantial subject see BREWER, J.G., *Enclosures and the Open Fields*, 1972.

14. TAYLOR, C., *The Cambridgeshire Landscape*, 1973, pp.143–9; STEANE, J.M., *The Northamptonshire Landscape*, 1974, pp.186–7.

15. PYE, N., *Leicester and its Region*, 1972, p.252.

16. BERESFORD, M.W. and ST JOSEPH, J.K.S., *Mediaeval England, an Aerial Survey*, 1958, p.121; RAISTRICK, A., *The West Riding of Yorkshire*,

1970, pp.72–4; ALLISON, K.J., *The East Riding of Yorkshire Landscape*, 1976, p.128; TAYLOR, C., *Fields in the English Landscape*, 1976, p.113.

17. RAISTRICK, A., *The West Riding of Yorkshire*, 1970, pp.74–5.

18. For a county study of these commissioners see TURNER, M., 'Enclosure Commissioners and Buckinghamshire Parliamentary Enclosure,' *Agricultural History Review*, 1977, pp.120–9. The most active of them, John Fellows, was as commissioner, surveyor and umpire 'partly responsible for fashioning the road and field pattern and subsequent farm pattern' of about 13% of the county' (p.126).

19. Clare was born in 1793 and published *Poems Descriptive of Rural Life and Scenes* and *The Village Minstrel* in 1821, *The Shepherd's Calendar* in 1827. For maps of Helpston, his native parish, in 1779, showing the open fields and some old enclosed fields, and in 1827, showing the 'regimented parliamentary pattern' of rectangular fields which followed enclosure under an Act of 1809 see STEANE, J.M., *The Northamptonshire Landscape*, 1974, p.234.

20. TAYLOR, C., *The Cambridgeshire Landscape*, 1973, p.182.

21. For the process of parliamentary enclosure see ADDY, J., *The Agrarian Revolution*, 1972, pp.25–35. For a case study of such an enclosure see LOUGHBOROUGH, B., 'An Account of a Yorkshire Enclosure, Staxton, 1803,' *Agricultural History Review*, 1965, pp.106–113. For a county study of enclosure see TURNER, M., 'Enclosure Commissioners and Buckinghamshire Parliamentary Enclosure', *Agricultural History Review*, 1977, pp.120–9. See also TATE, W.E., *A Domesday of English Enclosure Acts and Awards*, Reading University Library, 1978.

22. WATERS, C.M., *An Economic History of England*, 1928, p.316; HOSKINS, W.G., *The Making of the English Landscape*, 1955, p.157; HOSKINS, W.G., *Leicestershire*, 1957, p.100; BOVILL, E.W., *English Country Life*, 1780–1830, 1962, p.200; STEANE, J.M., *The Northamptonshire Landscape*, 1974, p.245.

23. ORWIN, C.S., *The Open Fields*, 1967; CHAMBERS, J.D., *Laxton, The Last Open Field Village*, 1964. Interestingly, the landscape of Laxton includes the results of enclosure by agreement, enclosures under the authority of an act of Parliament and of a comprehensive consolidation of stripholdings for greater efficiency.

24. For open field survivals see HOSKINS, W.G. and FINBERG, H.P.R., *Devonshire Studies*, 1952, pp.256–71; DAVIES, M., 'Rhosili Open Field and Related South Wales Field Patterns', *Agricultural History Review*, 1956, pp.80–96; BERESFORD, M.W. and ST JOSEPH, J.K.S., *Mediaeval England, An Aerial Survey*, 1958, pp.43–5; SCARFE, N., *The Suffolk Landscape*, 1972, p.181; BAKER, A.R.H. and BUTLIN, R.S. *Studies of Field Systems in the British Isles*, 1973, p.473, 507; FINBERG, H.P.R., *The Gloucestershire Landscape*, 1975, p.55; TAYLOR, C. *The Cambridgeshire*

Landscape, 1973, p.96; TAYLOR, C., *Fields in the English Landscape*, 1975, pp.87, 158, 159; WILLIAM, M., *The South Wales Landscape*, 1975, pp.86, 138; SLEE, A.H., *Victorian Days in a Devon Village*, 1978, p.6 (available from Braunton Museum.)

25. JENNINGS, P., *The Living Village*, 1972, p.46, quoting from the local Women's Institute scrapbook of 1965. See also BAKER, A.R.H. and BUTLIN, R.A., *Studies of Field Systems in the British Isles*, 1973, pp.512-15.

26. HOSKINS, W.G., *Fieldwork in History*, 1967, p.133 and RAISTRICK, A., *The West Riding of Yorkshire*, 1970, pp.67-70 for Linton; BAKER, A.R.H. and BUTLIN, R.A., *Studies of Field Systems in the British Isles*, 1973, p.48 and plan on p.89 for Liverpool. See also BALCHIN, W.G.V., *Cornwall*, 1954, p.36; DOBBIE, B.M.W., *An English Rural Community, Bathcaston with St Catharine*, 1969, p.135; ROWLEY, T., *The Shropshire Landscape*, 1972, p.140 for Stanton; BAKER, A.H.R. and BUTLIN, R.A., *Studies of Field Systems in the British Isles*, 1973, pp.506, 517; POLLARD, E., HOOPER, M.D. and MOORE, N.W., *Hedges*, 1974, pp.48, 49; MUNBY, L.M., *The Hertfordshire Landscape*, 1977, p.29 for Hatfield; GOSLING, S., *A Changing Landscape*, Oxfordshire County Council Museum Services, 1978, p.8 for Hampton Poyle and Islip.

27. TAYLOR, C., *The Cambridgeshire Landscape*, 1973, pp.95-6. For the value of raised headlands as evidence of field edges see BERESFORD, M.W., and ST JOSEPH, J.K.S., *Mediaeval England, an Aerial Survey*, 1958, pp.32-3; POCOCK, E.A., 'The First Fields in an Oxfordshire Parish', *Agricultural History Review*, 1968, pp.85, 94; BAKER, A.R.H., 'A Relatively Neglected Field Form; the Headland Ridge', *Agricultural History Review*, 1973, pp.47-50.

28. For the use of ridge-and-furrow for drainage see ORWIN, C.S., *The Open Fields*, 1967, pp.32-6 and TAYLOR, C., *Fields in the English Landscape*, 1975, pp.82-8. For the ridge-and-furrow on light land that does not require artificial drainage see MUNBY, L.M., *East Anglian Studies*, 1968, p.42; TAYLOR, C., *Fields in the English Landscape*, 1975, p.88. For the use of ridge-and-furrow to drain grassland see DAVIES, M., 'Rhosili open field and related South Welsh field patterns', *Agricultural History Review*, 1956, pp.95-6; DAVIES, C.S., *The Agricultural History of Cheshire, 1750-1850*, 1960, p.110; HALLAM, H.E., *Settlement and Society*, 1965, pp.139, 140, 151, 154.

29. FINBERG, H.P.R. (ed.), *The Agrarian History of England and Wales, AD 43 to 1042*, 1972, p.418.

30. For ridge-and-furrow which preserves the pattern of open field strips see BERESFORD, M., *The Lost Villages of England*, 1954, pp.48-53. For ridge-and-furrow 'which cannot be correlated with common arable fields' and a discussion of ridge-and-furrow as evidence on the open field system see BAKER, A.R.H. and BUTLIN, R.A., *Studies in Field Systems in the British Isles*, 1973, pp.34-5. Where ridge-and-furrow originated in open

fields, each ridge does not necessarily represent a strip occupied by an individual farmer. 'Each strip often comprised a number of ridges which probably varied in the course of time as they were sold, split up or amalgamated'. TAYLOR, C., *The Cambridgeshire Landscape*, 1973, p.93.

31. For seventeenth, eighteenth and early nineteenth century ridge-and-furrow see WISE, M.J., 'The decay of agriculture in a growing industrial area', *Agricultural History*, July 1953, p.145; HARRIS, H., *The Industrial Archaeology of Dartmoor*, 1968, p.145; BRANDON, P., *The Landscape of Sussex*, 1974, p.191; and TAYLOR, C., *Fields in the English Landscape*, 1975, p.126.

32. TRIST, P.J.O., 'Suffolk Marsh Reclamation Policy', *Agriculture*, October 1954, p.328; TRIST, P.J.O., *A Survey of the Agriculture of Suffolk*, 1971, p.184.

33. CLARK, H.M., 'Selion size and soil type', *Agricultural History Review*, 1960, pp.97–8. See also ALLISON, K.J., *The East Riding of Yorkshire Landscape*, 1976, p.154; RACKHAM, O., *Trees and Woodland in the British Landscape*, 1976, p.154.

34. TAYLOR, C., *Fields in the English Landscape*, 1976, p.111.

35. EYRE, S.R., 'The curving ploughstrip and its historical implications', *Agricultural History Review*, 1955, pp.80–94. See also BERESFORD, M.W., and ST JOSEPH, J.K.S., *Mediaeval England, an Aerial Survey*, 1958, p.121; EDWARDS, K.C., SWINNERTON, H.H. and HALL, R.H., *The Peak District*, 1962, p.139; ORWIN, C.S., *The Open Fields*, 1967, p.34; TAYLOR, C., *Dorset*, 1970, p.128; TAYLOR, C., *The Cambridgeshire Landscape*, 1973, p.143; BRANDON, P., *The Landscape of Sussex*, 1974, pp.123, 148; POLLARD, E., HOOPER, M.D. and MOORE, N.W., *Hedges*, 1974, p.34; MUNBY, L.M., *The Hertfordshire Landscape*, 1977, pp.164, 170. Examples of straight ridge-and-furrow overlying S-curves found in Northamptonshire and the West Riding of Yorkshire presumably date from the replacement of oxen by horses (TAYLOR, C., *Fields in the English Landscape*, 1975, p.111.). There are, however, curved strips in various parts of South Wales which do not seem to have been formed by oxteam ploughing. 'All that can be said (of these strips) is that in the open arable fields curvature often increases with gradient and with the swell of the slope' (DAVIES, M., 'Rhosili open field and related South Wales field patterns', *Agricultural History Review*, 1956, pp.95–6).

36. For the Gog Magog Hills, see TAYLOR, C., *The Cambridgeshire Landscape*, 1973, p.98, for Worth Matravers. TAYLOR, C., *Fields in the English Landscape*, 1975, p.92. For lynchets generally see BEECHAM, A., 'A review of Balks as Strip Boundaries in the Open Fields', *Agricultural History Review*, 1956, p.30; WHITTINGTON, G., 'Towards a Terminology for Strip Lynchets', *Agricultural History Review*, 1967, pp.103–7; BAKER, A.R.H., and BUTLER, R.A., *Studies of Field Systems in the British Isles*, 1973, pp.36, 512; TAYLOR, C., *Fields in the English*

Landscape, 1975, pp.28–30, 88–92. For lynchets in particular areas see BALCHIN, W.G.V., *Cornwall*, 1954, p.41; FINBERG, H.P.R., *Gloucestershire*, 1955, p.41; EDWARDS, K.C., SWINNERTON, H.H. and HALL, R.H., *The Peak District*, 1962, p.162; HARRIS, H., *The Industrial Archaeology of Dartmoor*, 1968, p.147; RAISTRICK, A., *The Pennine Dales*, 168, p.85; DOBBIE, B.M.W., *An English Rural Community, Batheaston with St Catherine*, 1969, pp.134–5; RAISTRICK, A., *The West Riding of Yorkshire*, 1970, p.27; TAYLOR, C., *Dorset*, 1970, p.88; HARRIS, H., *Industrial Archaeology of the Peak District*, 1971, pp.137, 138; HALL, W.G. (ed.), *Man and the Mendips*, 1972, p.77; NEWTON, R., *The Northumberland Landscape*, 1972, p.93; TAYLOR, C., *The Cambridge Landscape*, 1973, p.97; BRANDON, P., *The Landscape of Sussex*, 1974, pp.44, 123, 189; *Essex Landscape, no. 1. Historic Features*, Essex County Council, 1974, p.8; TAYLOR, C., *Fields in the English Landscape*, 1975, p.155 (Dorset and Yorkshire); ALLISON, K.J., *The East Riding of Yorkshire Landscape*, 1976, pl. 9; MUNBY, L.M., *The Hertfordshire Landscape*, 1977, p.185.

37. WILLIAMS, M., *The South Wales Landscape*, 1975, pp.140–1 for Pembrokeshire; WILLIAMS, M., 'The Enclosure and Reclamation of the Mendip Hills, 1770–1870', *Agricultural History Review*, 1971, pp.65–81; ORWIN, C.S., and SELLICK, R.J., *The Reclamation of Exmoor Forest*, (1970).

38. ROWLEY, T., *The Shropshire Landscape*, 1972, p.160.

39. BERESFORD, M.W., and ST JOSEPH, J.K.S., *Mediaeval England, an Aerial Survey*, 1958, pp.93–5.

40. EVANS, G.E., *Ask the Fellows Who Cut the Hay*, 1956, p.204.

41. SYLVESTER, D., *The Rural Landscape of the Welsh Borderland*, 1969, p.54; see also WILLIAMS, M., *The South Wales Landscape*, 1975, p.136.

42. WILLIAMS, M., *The South Wales Landscape*, 1975, p.141.

43. EVANS, G.E., *The Pattern under the Plough*, 1966, p.133; TAYLOR, C., *The Cambridgeshire Landscape*, 1973, pp.83–4.

44. SYLVESTER, D., *The Rural Landscape of the Welsh Borderland*, 1969, p.144.

45. HARRIS, A., *The Rural Landscape of the East Riding of Yorkshire, 1700–1850*, 1961, p.21.

46. HARRIS, H., *Industrial Archaeology of the Peak District*, 1971, pp.141–2, which includes a list of local examples.

47. For the belief in England see EVANS, G.E., *Ask the Fellows Who Cut the Hay*, 1956, pp.241–2. For the similar belief in Wales in the 'ty-annos' see WILLIAMS, M., *The South Wales Landscape*, 1975, p.139. References to these widespread beliefs occur frequently in the literature.

48. TAYLOR, C., *Dorset*, 1970, p.154.

49. EVANS, G.E., *Ask the Fellows Who Cut the Hay*, 1956, pp.241–2. One cottage on Blaxhall Common had been a pigsty within living memory.

50. For a Shropshire example see BERESFORD, M.W. and ST JOSEPH, J.K.S., *Mediaeval England, an Aerial Survey*, 1958, pp.93–5.

51. WILLIAMS, M., 'The Enclosure and Reclamation of the Mendip Hills, 1770 to 1870', *Agricultural History Review*, 1971, p.78.

52. DAVIES, C.S., *The Agricultural History of Cheshire, 1750–1850*, 1960, p.10; HOSKINS, W.G., *History from the Farm*, 1970, p.131, referring to South Lancashire; WILLIAMS, M., *The Draining of the Somerset Levels*, 1970, p.189; ALLISON, K.J., *The East Riding of Yorkshire Landscape*, 1976, p.155.

53. BRANDON, S., *The Landscape of Sussex*, 1974, p.190.

54. TAYLOR, C., *The Cambridgeshire Landscape*, 1973, p.185; MUNBY, L.M. (ed.), *East Anglian Studies*, 1968, p.29. See also MOREAU, *The Departed Village*, 1968, p.20 (Berrick Prior, Oxfordshire); MUNBY, L.M., *East Anglian Studies*, 1968, p.31; ROWLEY, T., *The Shropshire Landscape*, 1972, p.75; SCARFE, N., *The Suffolk Landscape*, 1972, pp.181, 189; TAYLOR, C., *The Cambridgeshire Landscape*, 1973, p.79.

55. BAKER, A.R.H. and BUTLIN, R.A., *Studies of Field Systems in The British Isles*, 1973, p.480. See also *Report of Royal Commission on Common Land*, 1955–1958, HMSO, 1958. For survivals of common grazing rights, see EVANS, G.E., *The Days We have Seen*, 1975, pp.45–7, 53–5 and BAKER, A.R.H. and BUTLIN, R.A., *Studies in Field Systems in the British Isles*, 1973, p.502; FOSTER, A.M., 'The Hitchin Cow Commoners', *Hertfordshire's Past*, Autumn 1978, pp.16–19. For the importance of grazing rights in dispute between the commoners of Northam in Devon and the County Council see the *Guardian*, 5 July 1979, p.2.

56. EVANS, G.E., *The Days We Have Seen*, 1975, pp.55–6. BUTCHER, D.R., *The Waveney Valley*, East Anglian Magazine Ltd, 1975, p.48 for the survival of the stakes.

57. RAISTRICK, A., *The Pennine Walls*, 1976, p.5.

58. EVANS, G.E., *The Days We Have Seen*, 1975, p.49 for the East Anglian examples, in a chapter on survivals of communal pastures in that area; 'Pixey Mead and Waterey Molly', *Country Life*, 28 September 1972, p.752 for Yarnton survival.

59. BOVILL, E.W., *English Country Life*, 1780–1830, 1962, p.199. See also HOSKINS, W.G., 'The Anatomy of the English Countryside', *Listener*, 29 April 1954, p.734, for Ab Kettleby; HOSKINS, W.G., 'History by the Hedge', *Farmers Weekly*, 1 August 1969, p.79; HARRIS, A., *The Rural Landscape of the East Riding of Yorkshire, 1700–1850*, 1961, for Kilham.

60. TAYLOR, C., *Fields in the English Landscape*, 1975, p.41.

61. BALCHIN, W.G., *Cornwall*, 1954, p.49.

62. HOSKINS, W.G., 'History by the Hedge', *Farmers Weekly*, 1 August

1969, p.79; HOSKINS, W.G., *Fieldwork in Local History*, 1967, p.123; POLLARD, E., HOOPER, M.D. and MOORE, N.W., *Hedges*, 1974, p.55; STEANE, J.M., *The Northamptonshire Landscape*, 1974, p.173; TAYLOR, C., *Fields in the English Landscape*, 1975, pp.115–17.

63. POLLARD, E., HOOPER, M.D., and MOORE, N.W., *Hedges*, 1974, pp.50, 55.

64. HOSKINS, W., *Talpa*, 1857, p.42. See also POLLARD, E., HOOPER, M.D. and MOORE, N.W., *Hedges*, 1974, p.55. For the adaptation of field systems to the needs of steam cultivation see ORWIN, C.S., *Progress in English Farming Systems, VIII, Pioneers in power farming*, 1934, pp.4–5; SCOTT WATSON, J.A., *History of the Royal Agricultural Society of England*, 1939, p.92; SPENCE, C.C., *God Speed The Plow*, University of Illinois, 1961, p.122.

65. There are, however, occasional exceptions. In Brecon hedges are often curved, as farmers believed that such curved hedges gave livestock better protection than straight hedges (WILLIAMS, M., *The South Wales Landscape*, 1975, p.137).

66. WILLIAMS, M., *The South Wales Landscape*, 1975, p.132.

67. RACKHAM, O., *Trees and Woodlands in the British Landscape*, 1976, pp.166–7.

68. The classical description of this technique is given by its founding fathers, POLLARD, E., HOOPER, M.D. and MOORE, N.W., in *Hedges*, 1974, pp.79–85. For the use of hawthorn in Midland hedges by Hanoverian enclosers see HOSKINS, W.G., 'History by the Hedge', *Farmers Weekly*, 1 August 1969, p.79; POLLARD, E., HOOPER, M.D. and MOORE, M.W., *Hedges*, 1974, p.93; STEANE, J.M., *The Northamptonshire Landscape*, 1974, p.233.

69. MUSGROVE, P., 'Hedges in History', *Money, Milk and Milestones*, Hendon and District Archaeological Society, 1976, pp.24–8. See also HEWLETT, G., 'Reconstructing a Historical Landscape from Field and Documentary evidence; Otford in Kent', *Agricultural History Review*, 1973, pp.94–110.

70. POLLARD, E., HOOPER, M.D. and MOORE, N.W., *Hedges*, 1974, p.28.

71. HOSKINS, W.G., *Fieldwork in Local History*, 1967, pp.18, 45, 128; HOSKINS, W.G., 'History by the hedge', *Farmers Weekly*, 1 August 1969, pp.78–9.

72. BARBER, D., *Farming and Wildlife*, 1969, p.83; *Hedges and Shelterbelts*, 1976, p.3. Nature Conservancy Council.

73. For hedges generally see POLLARD, E., HOOPER, M.D. and MOORE, N.W., *Hedges*, 1974; *Hedging*, The British Trust for Conservation Volunteers, 1975.

74. *Times*, 1 February 1978, p.4, reporting studies by the Department of Prehistory and Archaeology, Sheffield University.

75. HOSKINS, W.G. and FINBERG, H.P.R., *Devonshire Studies*, 1952, p.81. This is an assumption, but a convincing one.

76. MILLWARD, R., *Lancashire*, 1959, p.121.

77. ROLLINSON, W., *Lakeland Walls*, 1975, p.16; HOSKINS, W.G., in BBC TV 'The English landscape' programme, 22 January 1976.

78. DENT, A., 'The Last Wolf in England', *Countryman*, Spring 1974, p.49.

79. RAISTRICK, A., *The Pennine Walls*, 1976, pp.9–11, which quotes a 1788 Enclosure Award, and 13. HARRIS, H., *Industrial Archaeology of the Peak District*, 1971, pp.139, 145, contrasts walls built under the Enclosure Acts to required standards of height, width, slope and construction with earlier walls which were generally lower 'and of less specific construction'.

80. See, for example, the frontispiece map in RAISTRICK, A., *The Pennine Walls*, 1976. ROLLINSON, A., *Lakeland Walls*, 1975, pp.22–3, makes a similar distinction, but adds that 'without documentary proof, it is unwise to assign a date to these walls purely on the basis of the shape of the enclosure'.

81. TAYLOR, C., *Fields in the English Landscape*, 1976, p.100.

82. HOSKINS, W.G., *English Landscapes*, 1973, back cover.

83. TAYLOR, C., *Fields in the English Landscape*, 1976, p.128.

84. RAISTRICK, A., *The Pennine Walls*, 1976, pp.12–13.

85. EDWARDS, K., SWINNERTON, H.H. and HALL, R.H., *The Peak District*, 1972, p.139.

86. ROLLINSON, W., *Life and Tradition in the Lake District*, 1974, p.117. See also RAINSFORD-HANNAY, J., *Dry Stone Walling*, 1972; ROLLINSON, W., *Lakeland Walls*, 1975, RAISTRICK, A., *The Pennine Walls*, 1976; and the British Trust for Conservation Volunteers, *Dry Stone Walling*, 1977, The Drystone Walling Association, c/o Cally Estate Office, Gatehouse-of-Fleet, Scotland, publishes a bulletin and has issued a film strip on dry wall construction. See also EDWARDS, K.C., SWINNERTON, H.H. and HALL, R.H., *The Peak District*, 1962, pp.137–40; EDWARDS, K.C. (ed.), *Nottingham and its Regions*, 1966, p.216; HARRIS, H., *The Industrial Archaeology of Dartmoor*, 1968, p.153; HARTLEY, M. and INGILBY, J., *Life and Tradition in the Yorkshire Dales*, 1968, p.93; NEWTON, R., *The Northumberland Landscape*, 1972, pp.120, 127–8; PEARSALL, W.H. and PENNINGTON, W., *The Lake District*, 1972, pp.251–63; RAISTRICK, A., *The West Riding of Yorkshire*, 1972, p.77; BRILL, E., *Life and Tradition in the Cotswolds*, 1973, pp.146–8; HOSKINS, W.G., *English Landscapes*, 1973, pp.44, 86; ROLLINSON, W., *Life and Tradition in the Lake District*, 1974, pp.110–17; BUTCHART, M.C., 'Walls as fences', *Industrial Past*, Autumn 1976, pp.9–10; 'Stone walls and

appendages', booklet no. 16 issued by the Lake District National Park Information Service, 1977.

87. ACKERMAN, H., 'Barbed Wire', *Country Gentlemen's Estate Magazine*, March 1955, p.92.

88. There is apparently no historical interest in barbed wire in this country and no collection of early types of such wire. In the USA, however, interest in collecting historical examples of barbed wire is sufficient to maintain *The American Barbed Wire Journal*, published from Box 368, Texline, Texas. For the development of barbed wire in the USA, see DANHOF, C.H., 'The Fencing Problem in the 1850s', *Agricultural History*, 1944, pp.168–85, and ACKERMAN, H., 'Barbed Wire', *Country Gentlemens' Estate Magazine*, March 1955, pp.89–93; for a catalogue of all types of barbed wire patented in the USA, see CLIFTON, R., *Barbs, prongs, points, prickers and stickers*, University of Oklahoma, 1970. The John Judkyn Memorial, Freshford Manor, Bath, has 33 19th-century specimens of American barbed wire.

89. TAYLOR, C., *Fields in the English Landscape*, 1975, p.155.

90. TAYLOR, C., *Dorset*, 1970, pp.60, 62.

91. TAYLOR, C., *Fields in the English Landscape*, 1975, p.155.

92. POLLARD, E., HOOPER, M.D. and MOORE, N.W., *Hedges*, 1974, pp.84–5.

93. BERESFORD, M.W., *The Lost Villages of England*, 1954, pp.43–53.

94. This distinction is recognized explicity or implicitly by various historians. The terms used here are those of RACKHAM, O., *Trees and Woodland in the English Countryside*, 1976, p.17.

95. For an unusual early example of the planned landscape see RENNEL OF RODD, LORD, *Valley on the March*, 1958, pp.84–118, which reconstructs the development of the fieldsystem of the Hindwell valley in Herefordshire. This probably dates from before the Norman Conquest.

96. BRANDON, P., *The Landscape of Sussex*, 1974, p.99; NEWTON, R., *The Northumberland Landscape*, 1972, pp.120–8.

97. JOHNSON, S.A., 'Enclosure and changing agricultural landscapes in Lindsey', *Agricultural History Review*, 1963, p.98. Similarly, at Fornham All Saints in Suffolk, 'the basic agrarian landscape is the result of Parliamentary enclosure in 1804. But there are fragments of the open fields system to be seen. Under all this are the substantial remains of the prehistorical landscape of the second and third millenia B.C.' (MUNBY, L.M. (ed.), *East Anglian Studies*, 1968, p.26).

98. ROWLEY, T., *The Shropshire Landscape*, 1972, pp.103–4.

99. TAYLOR, C., *Dorset*, 1970, p.131.

100. ROLLINSON, W., *A History of Man in the Lake District*, 1967, p.121; PEARSALL, W. and PENNINGTON, W., *The Lake District*, 1973, p.251.

101. PEARSALL, W. and PENNINGTON, W., *The Lake District*, 1973, p.259.

102. ESSEX COUNTY COUNCIL, *Essex Landscape No. 1, Historic Features*, 1974, p.25.

103. POSTGATE, M.R., 'The Field System of Breckland', *Agricultural History Review*, 1962, p.96.

104. TAYLOR, C., *Dorset*, 1970, p.205. For current developments in landscape study see DEPARTMENT OF GEOGRAPHY, POLYTECHNIC OF NORTH LONDON, *Historic Landscapes; identification, recording and management*, 1979.

Chapter Three

1. For the effects of watersupplies on Saxon and mediaeval settlement, see GRIGSON, G., *An English Farmhouse*, 1948, pp.14–15; HOSKINS, W.G. and FINBERG, H.P.R., *Devonshire Studies*, 1952, p.80; HOSKINS, W.G., 'Farmhouses and History', *History Today*, 7 May 1960, p.33; HAVINDEN, M.A., *Estate Villages*, 1966, pp.23, 25; HARRIS, H., *Industrial Archaeology of the Peak District*, 1971, p.139; JENNINGS, P., *The Living Village*, 1972, pp.293–4.

2. PARKER, R., *The Common Stream*, 1975, p.249; HARRIS, H., *Industrial Archaeology of the Peak District*, 1971, pp.146–7.

3. FUSSELL, G.E., 'The Reclamation of the Wolds', *Journal of the Chartered Land Agents Society*, April 1954, p.161; HARRIS, A., *The Rural Landscape of the East Riding of Yorkshire, 1700–1850*, 1961, p.72; WILLIAMS, M., 'The enclosure and reclamation of the Mendip Hills, 1770–1850', *Agricultural History Review*, 1971, p.80; LAWE, C.R., *Farmers Weekly*, 1 October 1976, p.42; ALLISON, K.J., *The East Riding of Yorkshire*, 1977, p.56.

4. *Journal of the Royal Agricultural Society of England*, 1887, p.51, and 1896, p.556 for hydraulic rams; WINDER, T., *Handbook of Farm Buildings*, 1908, p.5; BRUNNER, H. and MAJOR, J.K., 'Water Raising by Animal Power', *Industrial Archaeology*, 1972, pp.117–51.

5. HENDERSON, G., *The Farming Ladder*, 1956, p.15.

6. HMSO, *National Farm Survey of England and Wales, 1941–1943*, 1946, p.61. For village water supplies generally see VINCE, J., *Wells and Water Supply*, 1978.

7. MARTIN, E.A., *Dewponds, History, Observation and Experiment*, 1915; PUGSLEY, A.J., *Dewponds, Fact and Fable*, 1939; WHITLOCK, R., 'Debunking the Dewpond', *Countryman*, Winter 1971/2, pp.131–5.

8. For the temperature of water from Exmoor springs and its value for the watermeadows which Frederic Knight installed there in early Victorian times see ORWIN, C.S. and SELLICK, R.J., *The Reclamation of Exmoor*, 1970, pp.107–8.

9. DAVIS, T., *General View of the Agriculture of Wiltshire*, 1811, p.122; FRY, A.H., *The Land of Britain. Report of the Land Utilisation Survey of Great Britain, pt.87, Wiltshire*, 1940, pp.180-4, including a map of the water-meadows of the Upper Avon basin on p.181; FUSSELL, G.E., *The Farmer's Tools*, 1952, p.18; FUSSELL, G.E., 'A watercure for hill grazings', *Journal of the Chartered Land Agents Society*, June 1954, pp.262-5, which refers to the watermeadows served by a canal on p.264; GOODLAND, N., *Farm Mechanisation*, July 1960, p.241; STAMP, L.D., *The Land of Britain*, 1962, pp.78-81 which includes on p.79 a drawing of a typical watermeadow system; JONES, E.L., 'Eighteenth Century Changes in Hampshire Chalkland Farming' *Agricultural History Review*, 1960, pp.6-8; FINBERG, E. (ed.), *Agrarian History of England and Wales, 1500-1640*, 1967, pp.100-101, 179-182; ORWIN, C.S. and SELLICK, R.J., *The Reclamation of Exmoor*, 1970, pp.107-8, including reference to watermeadows on Exmoor on p.107; TAYLOR, C., *Dorset*, 1970, pp.131-2, 136, 150, 152 who quotes on p.152 Hardy's description in *The Return of the Native* of 'meadows watered on a plan so rectangular that on a fine day they seem like a silver gridiron'; TAYLOR, C., *The Cambridgeshire Landscape*, 1973, pp.175-7; TAYLOR, C., *Fields in the English Landscape*, 1975, pp.134-8; BETTEY, J.H., 'The Development of Watermeadows in Dorset during the Seventeenth Century', *Agricultural History Review*, 1977, pp.37-42; WARREN, D., 'Waterpower on Farms in West Somerset', *Journal of the Somerset Industrial Archaeological Society*, no. 1, (1978), p.5. *The Agricultural Community in Shropshire*, Salop County Museum Information Sheet No. 2, n.d., p.1.

10. For the decline of the system and its remains see FRY, A.H., *The Land of Britain, Report of the Land Utilisation Survey of Great Britain, pt.87, Wiltshire*, 1940, pp.183-4; GOODLAND, N., *Farm Mechanisation*, July 1960, p.241; BARBER, D., *Farming and Wildlife*, 1970, p.83; TAYLOR, C., *Dorset*, 1970, p.131; TAYLOR, C., *The Cambridgeshire Landscape*, 1973, pp.175-7; TAYLOR, C., *Fields in the English Landscape*, 1975, p.136; BETTEY, J.H., 'The Development of Water Meadows in Dorset during the Seventeenth Century', *Agricultural History Review*, 1977, p.43. A 17th century scheme near Salisbury, still in operation in the 1950s, is described with illustrations in *Farmer and Stockbreeder*, 6 April 1954, pp.71-2; for schemes surviving into the 1960s and 1970s in Dorset and Hampshire see *Farmers Weekly*, 3 December 1971, p.XXII and HARRIS, H., 'Reconsidering the Watermeadows', *Field*, 26 August 1976, pp.432-3; the four watermeadow systems still in operation in Dorset, Hampshire and Wiltshire in 1978 include schemes at Bardolf Manor, Puddletown, Dorset and Court Farm, Lower Woodland, Salisbury. The author wishes to thank the officials of the Ministry of Agriculture, Fisheries and Food in Dorset, Hampshire and Wiltshire, who provided him with information on past and present schemes, and Bardolf Farms Ltd and Mr R. Edwards, who have allowed him to mention their systems. There is also a scheme still in operation at Curford Farm, near Williton, Somerset (WARREN, D., 'Waterpower on Farms in

West Somerset', *Journal of the Somerset Industrial Archaeological Society*, no. 1, (1978), p.5).

11. DENISON, J.D., 'On the Duke of Portland's Watermeadows at Clipstone Park', *Journal of the Royal Agricultural Society of England*, 1840, pp.359-70; EDWARDS, H.C., *The Land of Britain, Report of the Land Utilisation Survey of Great Britain*, pt. 60, *Nottinghamshire*, 1944, pp.531-2; SMITH, E.J., 'Wet Sand and Dry Sand', *Farmer's Weekly*, 2 June 1950, pp.54-8.

12. PAWSON, H.C., *Robert Bakewell*, 1957, pp.18, 79-81; Bakewell's irrigated meadows are now part of a sports field (COX, S., 'Back to Bakewell', *Farmers Weekly*, 3 December 1976, p.XIV). Remains of an irrigation scheme, probably dating from the 17th century, serving 30 acres at Brant Hall, Warley, survived into the 1930s (GAUT, R.C., *A History of Worcestershire Agriculture*, 1939, pp.123-4).

Chapter Four

1. HARRIS, H., *The Industrial Archaeology of Dartmoor*, 1968, p.149.

2. MANNERING, J., *Country Life*, 5 December 1957, p.1232.

3. MANSFIELD, W.S., *The Farmers Friend*, 1947, pp.21-2.

4. For deneholes see ADDISON, W., *The Thames Estuary*, 1954, pp.149-50, who estimates that the deneholes in Hangmans Wood near Rainham represent the excavation of 100,000 tons of marl, though some of this may have been used not on farms but to repair seawalls, and LEGEAR, R., *Subterranea Britannica*, Bulletin 6, August 1977, p.12. For marl generally see DAVIES, C.S., *The Agricultural History of Cheshire, 1750-1850*, 1960, p.110; EVANS, G.E., *Ask the Fellow who Cuts the Hay*, 1956, pp.84, 110, 191; WADE MARTIN, S., *The Holkham Estate in the 19th Century, with Special Reference to Farm Building and Agricultural Improvement*, unpublished dissertation submitted to University of East Anglia for degree of Doctor of Philosophy, 1975, pp.22-5, quoted by kind permission of the author.

5. BRANDON, P., *The Sussex Landscape*, 1974, p.194.

6. For marling and chalking and their surviving evidences see GARDNER, H.W. and GARNER, H.V., *The use of lime in British agriculture*, 1953, pp.14, 18, 19; FUSSELL, G.E., 'Marl, an Ancient Manure', *Nature*, 24 January 1959, pp.214-7; JESSE, R.H.B., *Survey of the Agriculture of Sussex*, 1960, p.27; HARRIS, A., *The Rural Landscape of the East Riding of Yorkshire, 1700-1850*, 1961, p.117; BOWEN, H.C., *Ancient Fields*, 1962, pp.31-2; PRINCE, H.C., 'The Origins of Pits and Depressions in Norfolk', *Geography*, 1964, pp.15-32; GARDNER, H.W., *Survey of the Agriculture of Hertfordshire*, 1967, pp.55, 108, 127-8; MUNBY, L.M., *East Anglian Studies*, 1968, p.68; LONG, W.H., *Survey of the Agriculture of*

Yorkshire, 1969, p.19; BAKER, A.R.H. and BUTLIN, R.A., *Studies of Fieldsystems in the British Isles*, 1973, pp.55–60, 241, 282, 420; BRANDON, P., *The Sussex Landscape*, 1974, pp.192–5; ARMSTRONG, D., *The Changing Landscape*, 1975, pp.104–6; ADDISON, K.J., *the East Riding of Yorkshire*, 1976, p.200; PALLISER, D.M., *The Staffordshire Landscape*, 1976, p.82.

7. GARDNER, H.W. and GARNER, H.V., *The Use of Lime in British Agriculture*, 1953, p.14; HARRIS, H., *Industrial Archaeology of the Peak District*, 1971, pp.61–4; WILLIAMS, M., *The South Wales Landscape*, 1975, p.157.

8. ATKINSON, F., *Industrial Archaeology of North-east England*, vol. I, 1974, pp.102; JOBEY, G., 'A note on sow-kilns', *Journal of the University of Newcastle on Tyne Agricultural Society*, 1966, pp.37–8, which includes references to surviving traces on p.38.

9. JESSE, R.H.B., *Survey of the Agriculture of Sussex*, 1960, p.27; RAISTRICK, A., *The Pennine Dales*, 1968, p.114; HARRIS, H., *Industrial Archaeology of the Peak District*, 1971, p.64.

10. ORWIN, C.S. and SELLICK, R.J., *The Reclamation of Exmoor*, 1970, pp.61–2, 102–5, 209; HARRIS, H., *Industrial Archaeology of the Peak District*, 1971, p.148; WILLIAMS, M., 'The Enclosure and Reclamation of the Mendip Hills, 1770–1850', *Agricultural History Review*, 1971, pp.69, 70, 81; BEASLEY, W., *Madocks and the Wonder of Wales*, 1967, p.134; WILLIAMS, M., *The South Wales Landscape*, 1975, pp.157–9.

11. For lime and farm kilns see GARDNER, H.W. and GARNER, H.V., *The Use of Lime in British Agriculture*, 1953, p.20; POWELL, D.J., 'Herefordshire Lime Kilns', *Countryman*, Autumn 1970, pp.52–4; RAISTRICK, A., *The West Riding of Yorkshire*, 1970, p.157; HARRIS, H., *Industrial Archaeology of the Peak District*, 1971, pp.60–4; WILLIAMS, M., *The South Wales Landscape*, 1974, p.228; JONES, J. and J., 'Limeburning in Norfolk', *Journal of the Norfolk Industrial Archaeology Society*, 1977, pp.21–31; WARD, A.P., 'A Limekiln near Fitzhead', *Journal of the Somerset Archaeological Society*, no.1, (1978), pp.39–43, also p.46. But not all ruins are those of farm kilns. ATKINSON, F., *Industrial Archaeology of North-east England*, vol. 1, 1974, p.103, considers that most surviving small 18th and 19th century kilns in this area were probably operated commercially. So, apparently, were the coastal lime kilns of North Devon (*Industrial Archaeology*, 1968, pp.208–10). In 1979 the Chalk Pits Museum of Industrial History, which includes some lime-burning kilns, was opened on the South Downs, near Amberley, Sussex.

Chapter Five

1. For field drainage generally see FUSSELL, G.E., 'The Evolution of field drainage', *Journal of the Bath and West and Southern Counties Society*, 1959/60, pp.59–72; FUSSELL, G.E., *The Farmer's Tools*, 1952, pp.15–34; HARVEY, N., *Ditches, Dykes and Deep Drainage*, 1956; FUSSELL, G.E., 'Field Drainage', *Journal of the Chartered Land Agents Society*, October 1959, pp.361–71; BRIGHTEN, C.W., 'Some Notes on Victorian Land Drainage Schemes', *Journal of the Chartered Land Agents Society*, April 1960, pp.158–9, which includes a list of relevant legislation; HOELSCHER, L.V., 'Improvements in Fencing and Drainage in Mid-19th century England', *Agricultural History*, 1963, pp.76–8; SCOURFIELD, E., *The Agricultural Gallery at the Welsh Folk Museum*, The National Museum of Wales, Welsh Folk Museum, 1976, pp.3–4; MINISTRY OF AGRICULTURE, FISHERIES AND FOOD, ADAS LAND DRAINAGE SERVICE, *History of Agricultural Drainage*, 1977, including estimate of drainage needs on p.8.

2. HARVEY, N., *Ditches, Dykes and Deep Drainage*, 1966, p.8.

3. *Journal of Ministry of Agriculture*, February 1925, pp.986–8 and July 1925, p.360; EVANS, G.E., *Ask the Fellows Who Cut the Hay*, 1956, p.120; EVANS, G.E., *Where Beards Wag All*, 1970, p.87; BLYTHE, R., *Listener*, 3 December 1970, p.788. See also HOELSCHER, L.V., 'Improvements in Fencing and Drainage in Mid-19th Century England', *Agricultural History*, 1963, p.76.

4. A bush drain laid in the 1920s, however, was still working a quarter of a century later (WRIGHT, P.A., *Old Farm Implements*, 1961, p.74).

5. JEWELL, C.A., *Victorian Farming*, 1975, p.131.

6. HARVEY, N., 'Relics of a Great Achievement', *Journal of the Chartered Land Agents Society*, October 1955, pp.475–7; LIVESLEY, M.C., *Field Drainage*, 1960, p.2. Some of the stone drains laid in the Glossop area in the 1860s were 'moderately effective' in the present decade, (HARRIS, H., *Industrial Archaeology of the Peak District*, 1971, p.198) and stone drains of unknown date at Great House Farm in Lancashire (one of the experimental husbandry farms of the Ministry of Agriculture, Fisheries and Food) were partly operational a few years ago (*Great House Experimental Farm*, issued by the Farm, 1960, pp.18–19).

7. HARTLEY, M. and INGILBY, J., *Life and tradition in the Yorkshire Dales*, 1968, p.95; COOPER, T., *Practical Land Drainage*, 1965, p.130 for Midland survivals. See also HOELSCHER, L.V., 'Improvements in Fencing and Drainage in Mid-19th Century England', *Agricultural History*, 1963, p.76.

8. JEWELL, C.A., *Victorian Farming*, 1975, p.130. A variety of early tilepipes are illustrated in *Farmer's Weekly*, 20 April 1979, pp.88–9.

9. KENDALL, R.G., *Land Drainage*, 1950, p.14; HARVEY, N., 'Relics of a Great Achievement', *Journal of the Chartered Land Agents Society*, October 1955, pp.475–7; BRIGHTEN, C.W., 'Some Notes on Victorian Land

Drainage Schemes', *Journal of Chartered Land Agents Society*, 1960, p.160; LIVESLEY, M.C., *Field Drainage*, 1960, p.6; MERCER, W.B., *Survey of the Agriculture of Cheshire*, 1963, p.17; LOVELIDGE, B., *Farmers Weekly*, 4 December 1964, p.XV; CHARLTON, R., *Farmers Weekly*, 9 April 1965, pp.76–7; HOPE, H., *Farmers Weekly*, 9 May 1969, pp.56–8; JENNINGS, P., *The Living Village*, 1972, p.26; JOYCE, P.T., *Livestock Farming*, January 1976, p.15; HOPE, H., *Farmers Weekly*, 15 September 1978, p.XI. It is significant that four post-war textbooks, KENDALL, R.G., *Land Drainage*, 1950; NICHOLSON, H.H., *The Principles of Field Drainage*, 1953; LIVESLEY, M.C., *Field Drainage*, 1960; and COOPER, T., *Practical Land Drainage*, 1965, contain sections on the reconditioning of old (i.e. Victorian and earlier) schemes. The number and importance of such survivals is sufficient to make necessary an official leaflet on their restoration (MINISTRY OF AGRICULTURE, FISHERIES AND FOOD, *Old Under-drainage Systems*, Drainage Leaflet No. 12, 1973). This illustrates old tilepipes.

10. The relevant Acts are 24 Geo. 3 Sess. 2, c.24 (1784), 7 Geo. 4, c.49 (1826) and 13 and 14 Vict. c.9 (1850).

11. For contemporary estimates see PHILLIPS, A.D.M., 'Underdraining in the English claylands, 1850–1880. A review', *Agricultural History Review*, 1969, pp.44–45. The recent estimate is given in MINISTRY OF AGRI-CULTURE, FISHERIES AND FOOD, ADAS LAND DRAINAGE SERVICE, *History of Agricultural Drainage*, 1977, p.8.

Chapter Six

1. ORDISH, G., *Winegrowing in England*, 1953, pp.23–4; HURRY, J.B., *The Woad Plant and its Dye*, 1930, p.283.

2. DIMBLEBY, G.W., *Plants and Archaeology*, 1967; HELBAEK, H., 'Paleo-ethnology', *Science and Archaeology*, ed. BROTHWELL, D and HIGGS, E., 1970, pp.206–14; RENFREW, J.M., MONK, M. and MURPHY, P., *First aid for seeds*, Rescue, Hertford, 1975; REYNOLDS, P.J., *Farming in the Iron Age*, 1970, p.10; *Observer Magazine*, 27 May 1979, p.47 for the Woburn grasses.

3. For the development of agricultural plant breeding see ROBINSON, D.H., *The New Farming*, 1938, pp.35–56; BELL, G.D.H., *Cultivated Plants of the Farm*, 1948, pp.179–91; BELL, G.D.H., 'The Contribution of Plant Breeding to Crop Improvement', *Agriculture*, May 1951, pp.91–5; RILEY, R. 'Developments in Plant Breeding', *Agricultural Progress*, 1974, pp.1–16. For examples of the historical significance of changes in crop varieties, see the story of the Grey Oat in HUNTER, H., *Oats*, 1924, pp.13, 47 and FINDLAY, W.M., *Oats*, 1956, pp.5, 28 and of Chevallier barley in

BEAVEN, E.S., *Barley*, 1948, p.90 and HUNTER, H., *The Barley Crop*, 1952, p.68. See also PERCIVAL, J., *Wheat in Great Britain*, 1948, pp.78–87, 87, 89, 97, 101, 111, 116.

4. 'During the last fifty or sixty years there has been constant changing of the varieties in general cultivation and, with few exceptions, the old varieties have been replaced by improved varieties of more recent introduction'. (BELL, G.D.H., *Cultivated Plants of the Farm*, 1948, p.184).

5. SCOTT WATSON, J., 'English Agriculture in 1850/1', *Journal of the Royal Agricultural Society of England*, 1950, p.17.

6. MANSFIELD, W.S., *The Farmer's Friend*, 1947, pp.85–6 (for proverb); PEACHEY, R.A., *Cereal Varieties in Great Britain*, 1951, p.77; LAMBETH, M., *A Golden Dolly*, 1969, p.16.

7. See FRANKEL, O.H. and BENNETT, E., *Genetic Resources in Plants – their Exploration and Conservation*, 1970; HAWKES, J.G., 'Conservation of Plant Genetic Resources', *Outlook on Agriculture*, 1971, pp.248–53; LAWRENCE, E., 'Future in the past', *Nature*, 27 November 1975, pp.278–9; SIMMONDS, N.W., *Evolution of Cultivated Crops*, 1976; HAWKES, J.G., 'Plant Gene Pools', *Journal of the Royal Society of Arts*, April 1977, pp.224–35. For information on surviving varieties see WILLIAMS, J.T., *An Index of Living Plant Collections in the British Isles*, 1974, and *Supplement*, 1976; HAWKES, J.G., *A Bibliography of Plant Genetic Resources*, International Board of Plant Genetic Resources, Rome, 1976. The Butser Ancient Farm Project, which has reconstructed an Iron Age farm at Butser Hill, has collected seeds of a dozen types of cereal and other crops as similar as is now possible to those grown in the Iron Age and is preparing a seedbank which will allow their cultivation on a field scale (*The Iron Age Demonstration Area, Queen Elizabeth Country Park*, County Recreation Department, Winchester, 1976, pp.14–16).

8. An enquiry in 1973–4 found no stocks of agricultural seeds of historical interest held by seeds-merchants. Small quantities of some 30 historical varieties of cereals, beans, peas, and potatoes, which were grown in the 19th century and in a few cases earlier but are no longer cultivated, were kept at various official plant breeding stations (Personal experience in connection with the Old Fort William Project of National Heritage Ltd, Toronto.). It is, however, unlikely that any of these survivals are identical with their older ancestors as there has almost certainly been selection or other forms of improvement over the years.

Chapter Seven

1. RYDER, M.L., 'The History of Sheep Herds in Britain', *Agricultural History Review*, 1964, pp.1–12, 65–82, which includes on pp.68–9 a tabulated

summary of wool types found in 87 British parchments dating from the 12th to 19th centuries; RYDER, M.L., 'Life in Dead Sea Scrolls', *Countryman*, Winter 1969, pp.362–6; RYDER, M.L., 'The Origins and History of British Breeds of Sheep', *The Ark*, 15 June 1976, pp.166–72.

2. RYDER, M.L., 'Livestock Remains from Four Mediaeval Sites in Yorkshire', *Agricultural History Review*, 1961, pp.105–10; RYDER, M.L., *Animal Bones in Archaeology*, 1968; RYDER, M.L., 'Old bones', *Countryman*, Spring 1969, pp.109–14; CHAPLIN, R.E., *The Study of Animal Remains from Archaeological Sites*, 1971; CORNWALL, R.E., *Bones for Archaeologists*, 1974; RYDER, M.L., 'The Origins and History of British Breeds of Sheep', *The Ark*, 15 June 1976, pp.166–72.

3. 'English Animals Abroad', *Field and Farm, The Collected Essays of Richard Jefferies*, ed. LOOKER, S.J., 1957, pp.159, 162. This essay was written in 1877.

4. For the history of British livestock see PAWSON, H.C., *Robert Bakewell*, 1957; TROW SMITH, R., *A History of British Livestock Husbandry to 1700*, 1957; TROW SMITH, R., *A History of British Livestock Husbandry, 1700–1900*, 1959.

5. HUDSON, W.H., *A Shepherd's Life*, 1979, pp.14–15.

6. BOWMAN, J.C. and AINDOW, C.T., *Genetic Conservation and the Less Common Breeds of British Cattle, Sheep and Pigs*, 1973, pp.30–1.

7. ALDERSON, L., *The Observer's Book of Farm Animals*, 1976, p.124.

8. BOWMAN, J.C. and AINDOW, C.T., *Genetic Conservation and the Less Common Breeds of British Cattle, Sheep and Pigs*, 1973, p.15.

9. SHEPPY, A.J., 'The Domestic Fowl', *The Ark*, 15 October 1974, pp.12–15; ALDERSON, L., *The Observer's Book of Farm Animals*, 1976, p.173; HAMS, F., *Old Poultry Breeds*, 1978.

10. WHITEHEAD, G.K., *The Ancient White Cattle of Britain and their Descendants*, 1953; WHITEHEAD, G.K., *Ancient White Cattle*, 1963; *The Ark*, May 1974, pp.5–6; *The Ark*, 15 December 1974; *The Ark*, May 1974, pp.5–6, 15 June 1974, p.4 (for wartime transfer), 15 December 1974, pp.20–2; ALDERSON, L., *The Observer's Book of Farm Animals*, 1976, pp.138–9.

11. *The Ark*, 15 July 1974, p.3.

12. BOWMAN, J.C. and AINDOW, C.T., *Genetic Conservation and the Less Common Breeds of British Cattle, Pigs and Sheep*, 1973, p.33; RAYNS, F., *The Ark*, 'Norfolk Horn Sheep', 15 January 1975, p.7; *The Ark*, 15 December 1975, pp.318–24; *The Ark*, 15 February 1976, pp.54–6.

13. BOWMAN, J.C. and AINDOW, C.T., *Genetic Conservation and the Less Common Breeds of British Cattle, Sheep and Pigs*, 1973, p.23; *The Ark*, 15 July 1974, p.6; *The Ark*, 15 August 1974, pp.10–11.

14. ALDERSON, L., *The Chance to Survive*, 1978. Information obtained by surveys on rare breeds and their numbers are given in BOWMAN, J.C. and

AINDOW, C.T., *Genetic Conservation and the Less Common Breeds of British Cattle, Pigs and Sheep*, 1973, p.14 and *The Ark*, 15 May 1975, pp.109–12. For a bibliography see *The Ark, Index to Volumes I–IV, 1974–1977*, 1978, pp.6–13. See also VINCE, J., *Old British Livestock*, 1974 and JEWELL, P.A. and ALDERSON, G.L.H., 'Genetic Considerations in Domestic Animals; Purposes and Actions to preserve Rare Breeds', *Journal of the Royal Society of Arts*, October 1977, pp.693–710.

The numerous breed societies, including those for rare or threatened breeds, publish information in various forms. The addresses of these societies are given in the *British Farmer and Stockbreeder's Yearbook and Farm Diary*. The Rare Breeds Survival Trust, Winkleigh, Devon, publishes *The Ark* journal, which includes information on such breeds and on shows, demonstrations and farm parks where examples can be seen. A list of such farm parks is given in each issue. The Rare Breeds Society, The Homestead, High Street, Congresbury, Bristol, is concerned with the preservation of endangered breeds of poultry.

Chapter Eight

1. FINBERG, H.P.R. (ed.), *The Agrarian History of England and Wales, 1500–1640*, 1967, pp.431–2; MOREAU, R.E., *The Departed Village*, 1968, pp.70–1, 117, 131; *Complete Catalogue of the Royal Show*, issued annually by the Royal Agricultural Society of England, gives figures on exhibits at previous shows in introductory pages.

2. *Stanmer*, Stanmer Preservation Society, n.d. but post 1973, p.26.

3. JEWELL, A., *Victorian Farming*, 1975, pp.129–30 and KENDALL, R.G., *Field Drainage*, 1950, p.97 provide a comparison of 19th century and modern drainers' tools. For drainage tools and machines for making tilepipes see SCOTT WATSON, J.A., *History of the Royal Agricultural Society of England*, 1939, pp.30, 32, 86–7; FUSSELL, G.E., *The Farmer's Tools*, 1952, pp.23, 27; FUSSELL, G.E., 'Field Drainage', *Journal of the Chartered Land Agents Society*, October 1959, pp.361–72; PARTRIDGE, M., *Farm Tools through the Ages*, 1973, pp.16–23; SMEDLEY, N., *Life and Tradition in Suffolk and North-East Essex*, 1976, p.59; *The Farming Year in Suffolk, Museum of East Anglian Rural Life*, 1977, pp.1–3. For drainer's clogs with steel plates on the instep see HARTLEY, M. and INGILBY, J., *Life and Tradition in the Yorkshire Dales*, 1977, p.95 and *The Farming Year in Suffolk*, Museum of East Anglian Life, 1977, p.1.

4. FUSSELL, G.E., *The Farmer's Tools*, 1952, pp.22–7.

5. COOPER, T., *Practical Land Drainage*, 1965, pp.39–41; FUSSELL, G.E., 'Field Drainage', *Journal of the Chartered Land Agents Society*, October 1959, pp.367–9.

6. *Journal of Ministry of Agriculture*, July 1925, p.303; NICHOLSON, H.H., *The Principles of Land Drainage*, 1953, p.9.

7. NICHOLSON, H.H., *The Principles of Land Drainage*, 1953, p.11; *Farmer's Weekly*, 5 May 1978, Drainage Supplement, pp.28–9. For the development of mole drainage see FUSSELL, G.E., *The Farmer's Tools*, 1952, pp.29–31; FUSSELL, G.E., 'Field Drainage', *Journal of the Chartered Land Agents Society*, October 1959, pp.361–72; BONNETT, H., *Farming with Steam*, 1974, pp.2–3, 41.

8. For hedging and hedger's tools see MANSFIELD, W.S., *The Farmer's Friend*, 1947, p.17; HARTLEY, M. and INGILBY, J., *Life and Tradition in the Yorkshire Dales*, 1968, pp.111–12; POLLARD, E., HOOPER, M.D. and MOORE, N.W., *Hedges*, 1974, pp.192–7; SCOURFIELD, E., *The Welsh Farming Scene*, National Museum of Wales, Welsh Folk Museum, 1974, pp.5–8; *Hedging*, British Trust for Conservation Volunteers, 1975; JENKINS, J.G., *Life and Tradition in Rural Wales*, 1976, p.31; SCOUR-FIELD, E., *The Agricultural Gallery at the Welsh Folk Museum*, National Museum of Wales, Welsh Folk Museum, 1976, pp.4–7; *The Farming Year in Suffolk*, Museum of East Anglian Rural Life, 1977, p.5.

9. *Farm Implement and Machinery Review*, February 1952, p.1586.

10. For dry stone walling and the tools used see HARTLEY, M. and INGILBY, J., *Life and Traditions in the Yorkshire Dales*, 1968, pp.93–4; *Dry Stone Dyking Training Film*, 1971, a film strip issued by the Dry Stone Walling Association, c/o Cally Estate Office, Gatehouse-of-Fleet, Scotland; RAINSFORD-HANNAY, J., *Dry Stone Walling*, 1972; ROLLINSON, W., *Lakeland Walls*, 1975, pp.6–10; RAISTRICK, A., *The Pennine Walls*, 1976, pp.12–20; *Drystone Walling*, British Trust for Conservation Volunteers, 1977.

11. VINCE, J., *Old Farm Tools*, 1974, pp.5–6.

12. *Farm Mechanisation*, April 1954, p.128.

13. FUSSELL, G.E., *The Farmer's Tools*, 1952, p.113; FUSSELL, G.E., 'Seed and Manure Drills', *Journal of the Chartered Land Agents Society*, 1959, pp.326–7; FUSSELL, G.E., 'Root planters and harvesters', *Journal of the Chartered Land Agents Society*, 1960, p.17.

14. The Saxon riddle is quoted in full in PASSMORE, J.B., *The English Plough*, 1930, pp.3–4.

15. GARRAD, G.H., *A Survey of the Agriculture of Kent*, 1954, pp.133–4.

16. SEEBOHM, M.E., *The Evolution of the English Farm*, 1952, p.328; JESSE, R.H.B., *A Survey of Agriculture in Sussex*, 1960, p.15.

17. *Ransome's Royal Records*, 1939, pp.23, 50. For the plough see PASSMORE, J.B., *The English Plough*, 1930; FUSSELL, G.E., *The Farmer's Tools*, 1952, pp.35–73; PAYNE, F.G., 'The British Plough. Some Stages in its Development', *Agricultural History Review*, 1957, pp.74–84; FUSSELL, G.E., 'Ploughs and ploughing', *Journal of the Chartered Land Agents Society*, July

1959, pp.253–62; *Ploughing through the Ages*, Royal Agricultural Society of England, 1966; BRILL, E., *Life and Tradition in the Cotswolds*, 1973, pp.66–70; ROLLINSON, W., *Life and Tradition in the Lakeland District*, 1974, pp.97–9; JENKINS, J.G., *Life and Tradition in Rural Wales*, 1976, pp.32, 35, 37; SCOURFIELD, E., *The Agricultural Gallery of the Welsh Folk Museum*, National Museum of Wales, Welsh Folk Museum, 1976, pp.8–11; SMEDLEY, N., *Life and Tradition in Suffolk and North-East Essex*, 1976, pp.61–6; *The Farming Year in Suffolk*, Museum of East Anglian Life, 1977, pp.9–18.

18. FUSSELL, G.E., 'The Breast Plough', *Man*, 1933, pp.109–14; TAYLOR, J.N., *City of Gloucester Folk Museum, Guide to Collection of Bygone Agricultural Implements*, 1950, p.4 for modern example; WRIGHT, P., *Old Farm Implements*, 1961, p.61; HIGGS, J., *The Land*, 1964, photo. 79; ARCHER, F., *The Distant Scene*, 1967, p.141 for Vale of Evesham; BRILL, E., *Life and Tradition in the Cotswolds*, 1973, p.70 for Gloucestershire; VINCE, J., *Old Farm Tools*, 1974, p.4. The breast plough also survived in Cumbria into the 19th century (ROLLINSON, W., *Life and Tradition in the Lake District*, 1974, pp.98–9).

19. The ringed Cambridge roller, which is still in use, was introduced in 1844. Incidentally, it is named after its inventor, not after the town (BLANDFORD, P., *Old Farm Tools and Machinery*, 1976, p.98). For survivals of older types of roller see BEECHAM, H.A. and HIGGS, J., *The Story of Farm Tools*, 1961, p.14; JENKINS, J.G., *Life and Tradition in Rural Wales*, 1976, p.32.

20. The zigzag harrow appeared in 1839, the chainlink harrow in 1840 (BEECHAM, H.A. and HIGGS, J., *The Story of Farm Tools*, 1961, p.13; PARTRIDGE, M., *Farm Tools through the Ages*, 1973, p.80). For survivals of older types of harrow see RAWSON, H.C., *A Survey of the Agriculture of Northumberland*, 1961, p.37; HALL, W.G., *Man and the Mendips*, 1972, p.79; JENKINS, J.G., *Life and Tradition in Rural Wales*, 1976, pp.32, 38.

21. FUSSELL, G.E., *The Farmer's Tools*, 1952, p.73; BEECHAM, H.A. and HIGGS, J., *The Story of Farm Tools*, 1961, p.13 for survivals; PARTRIDGE, M., *Farm Tools through the Ages*, 1973, pp.73–80; SMEDLEY, N., *Life and Tradition in Suffolk and North-East Essex*, 1976, p.67 for scarifier; BLANDFORD, P., *Old Farm Tools and Machinery*, 1976, pp.100–4; *The Farming Year in Suffolk*, The Museum of East Anglian Life, 1977, pp.23–6. The diskharrow was patented in the USA in 1857, but not extensively used in this country until the early 1900s (HUTCHINSON, T., *Machinery on the Farm*, 1949, p.53).

22. ROLLINSON, W., *Life and Tradition in the Lake District*, 1974, plates 74, 75; SCOURFIELD, E., *The Welsh Farming Scene*, Welsh National Museum, Welsh Folk Museum, 1974, pp.15, 16; JENKINS, J.G., *Life and Tradition in Rural Wales*, 1976, p.31, who describes the work of one of the last craftsmen making seedlips.

23. SCOURFIELD, W., *The Welsh Farming Scene*, National Museum of Wales, Welsh Folk Museum, 1974, p.16; TOULSON, S., *Discovering Farm Museums and Farm Parks*, 1977, p.20 and *Farmers Weekly*, 25 August, 1978, p.56 for fiddle survivals. For handsowing equipment see WRIGHT, D., 'Broadcast Sowing in England', *Countryman*, Spring 1970, pp.84–8; SMEDLEY, N., *Life and Tradition in Suffolk and North-East Essex*, 1976, pp.72–5; *The Farming Year in Suffolk*, Museum of East Anglian Life, 1977, pp.27–8. For a description of the handsowing of turnips see EVANS, G.E., *Ask the Fellows Who Cut the Hay*, 1956, p.88.

24. For the development of the drill see FUSSELL, G.E., *The Farmer's Tools*, 1952, pp.92–114; FUSSELL, G.E., 'Seed and Manure Drills', *Journal of the Chartered Land Agents Society*, September 1959, pp.318–27; VINCE, J., *Vintage Farm Machines*, 1973, pp.22–3; FUSSELL, G.E., *Jethro Tull. His Influence on the Mechanisation of Agriculture*, 1974.

25. BLANDFORD, P., *Old Farm Tools and Machinery*, 1976, p.101.

26. EVANS, G.E., *Ask the Fellows Who Cut the Hay*, 1956, pp.120–21 for Suffolk survivals; BEECHAM, H.A. and HIGGS, J., *The Story of Farm Tools*, 1961, p.17; JENKINS, J.G., *Life and Tradition in Rural Wales*, 1976, p.41; SMEDLEY, N., *Life and Tradition in Suffolk and North-East Essex*, 1976, pp.78–9; *The Farming Year in Suffolk*, Museum of East Anglian Life, 1977, pp.32–3; BRICK, A., *Farmers Weekly*, 20 October 1978, p.133 for Devon survivals.

27. COLLINS, E.J.T., *Sickle to Combine*, 1969, p.58; BRANDON, P., *The Sussex Landscape*, 1974, p.33; SCOURFIELD, E., *The Welsh Farming Scene*, National Museum of Wales, Welsh Folk Museum, 1974, p.25.

28. COLLINS, E.J.T., *Sickle to Combine*, 1969, p.58.

29. COLLINS, E.J.T., *Sickle to Combine*, 1969, p.58; ROLLINSON, W., *Life and Tradition in the Lake District*, 1974, p.10; SCOURFIELD, E., *The Welsh Farming Scene*, National Museum of Wales, Welsh Folk Museum, 1974, p.22.

30. COWLEY, B., *Farming in Yorkshire*, 1972, p.26.

31. For harvesting equipment see FUSSELL, G.E., *The Farmer's Tools*, 1952, pp.115–39; FUSSELL, G.E., 'Cereal and Seed Harvesting', *Journal of the Chartered Land Agents Society*, December 1959, pp.466–76; HARTLEY, M. and INGILBY, J., *Life and Tradition in the Yorkshire Dales*, 1968, p.70; COLLINS, E.J.T., *Sickle to Combine*, 1969, pp.10–22; VINCE, J., *Vintage Farm Machines*, 1973, pp.29–32; DE SEYSELL, B., 'The Art of Scything', *Countryman*, Autumn 1974, pp.155–60; ROLLINSON, W., *Life and Tradition in the Lake District*, 1974, pp.99–101; VINCE, J., *Old Farm Tools*, 1974, pp.23–5; JENKINS, J.G., *Life and Tradition in Rural Wales*, 1976, pp.41–6; SMEDLEY, N., *Life and Tradition in Suffolk and North-East Essex*, 1976, pp.80–93; *The Farming Year in Suffolk*, Museum of East Anglian Life, 1977, pp.35–41. For tools for making straw ropes see BRILL,

E., *Life and Tradition in the Cotswolds*, 1973, p.85 and *The Farming Year in Suffolk*, The Museum of East Anglian Life, 1977, p.44. For a living memory of scythe and sharpening stone see *Farmers Weekly*, 16 June 1978, p.125.

32. GARRATT, G.T., *Hundred Acre Farm*, 1928, p.125. For the last sheaf and the corn dolly see EVANS, G.E., *Ask the Fellows who Cut the Hay*, 1956, p.214; LAMBETH, M., *Discovering Corn Dollies*, 1974.

33. PAWSON, H.C., *A Survey of the Agriculture of Northumberland*, 1961, p.37.

34. For an engraving of a machine of this type at work from the 1888 edition of HENRY STEPHENS *Book of the Farm* see *The Farming Year in Suffolk*, The Museum of East Anglian Life, 1977, p.47. The scene shown was described as 'quite common up till 1860 and even later in some parts of the country'. SMEDLEY, N., *Life and Tradition in Suffolk and North-East Essex*, 1976, p.93, refers to a corndresser manufactured in 1839 and used till 1963.

35. For thrashing equipment see FUSSELL, G.E., *The Farmer's Tools*, 1952, pp.152–79; EVANS, G.E., *Ask the Fellows Who Cut the Hay*, 1956, pp.93–6; FUSSELL, G.E., 'Thrashing and Barn Machinery', *Journal of the Chartered Land Agents Society*, February 1960, pp.61–71; MOREAU, R.E., *The Departed Village*, 1968, p.77; COLLINS, E.J.T., *Sickle to Combine*, 1969, pp.35–41; KIMBELL, E.E., 'The Sound of Steam Thrashing', *Countryman*, Winter 1971–2, pp.152–8; BONNETT, H., *Farming with Steam*, 1974, pp.21–6; ROLLINSON, R., *Life and Tradition in the Lake District*, 1974, pp.31, 101–2; BONNETT, H., *Discovering Traction Engines*, 1975, pp.8–12; MACDONALD, S., 'The Progress of the Early Thrashing Machine', *Agricultural History Review*, 1975, pp.63–77; JENKINS, J.G., *Life and Tradition in Rural Wales*, 1976, pp.47–8; SCOURFIELD, E., *The Agricultural Gallery in the Welsh Folk Museum*, National Museum of Wales, Welsh Folk Museum, 1976, pp.29–31; SMEDLEY, N., *Life and Tradition in Suffolk and North-East Essex*, 1976, p.90.

36. EVANS, G.E., *Ask the Fellows Who Cut the Hay*, 1956, p.96; WRIGHT, P., *Old Farm Implements*, 1961, pp.34, 48; COLLINS, E.J.T., *Sickle to Combine*, 1969, p.35; COWLEY, B., *Farming in Yorkshire*, 1972, p.36; BRILL, E., *Life and Tradition in the Cotswolds*, 1973, pp.71–2; 155.

37. PAWSON, H.C., *A Survey of the Agriculture of Northumberland*, 1961, p.37; ATKINSON, F., 'An Open-air Museum in the North-East', *Industrial Archaeology*, 1964, p.4; *Country Life*, 12 March 1970, p.640; HARRISON, A. and HARRISON, J.K., 'The Horsewheel in North Yorkshire', *Industrial Archaeology*, 1973, p.262; SCOURFIELD, E., *The Welsh Farming Scene*, 1974, p.31.

38. The Bingfield engine is now in the private Westside Museum of Mr J.E. Moffit, CBE, at Stocksfield, Northumberland. It was erected on a farm in the same county c. 1835 to drive a thrashing machine and other barn machinery and continued in use until shortly after the First World War. In

the same area an 1852 steam-engine was used until about 1910 (ATKINSON, F., 'An Open-air Museum in the North-East', *Industrial Archaeology*, 1964, p.5). For the portable engine see KIMBELL, E.E., 'The Sound of Steam Thrashing', *Countryman*, Winter 1971-2, pp.154-8.

39. For haymaking equipment see FUSSELL, G.E., *The Farmer's Tools*, 1952, pp.139-51; FUSSELL, G.E., 'Haymaking and Grass Drying', *Journal of the Chartered Land Agents Society*, November 1959, pp.417-27; HARTLEY, M. and INGILBY, J., *Life and Tradition in the Yorkshire Dales*, 1968, p.77; VINCE, J., *Vintage Farm Machines*, 1973, pp.27-8; DE SEYSELL, B., 'The Art of Scything' *Countryman*, Autumn 1974, pp.155-60; VINCE, J., *Old Farm Tools*, 1974, p.20; ROLLINSON, W., *Life and Tradition in the Lake District*, 1974, pp.102-3; JENKINS, J.G., *Life and Tradition in Rural Wales*, 1976, pp.41-5; SMEDLEY, N., *Life and Tradition in Suffolk and North-East Essex*, 1976, p.88.

40. FEARN, J., *Thatch and Thatching*, 1976; SMEDLEY, N., *Life and Tradition in Suffolk and North-East Essex*, 1976, pp.47-52; *The Thatcher's Craft*, Council for Small Industries in Rural Areas, 1977; SMITH, D.J., *Discovering Country Crafts*, 1977, pp.7-12; *Guide* to Breamore Countryside Museum, n.d., p.21.

41. FUSSELL, G.E., *The Farmer's Tools*, 1952, pp.186-90; FUSSELL, G.E., 'Root Planters and Harvesters', *Journal of the Chartered Land Agents Society*, January 1960, pp.17-23; SCOURFIELD, E., *The Agricultural Gallery at the Welsh Folk Museum*, National Museum of Wales, Welsh Folk Museum, 1976, pp.15-16.

42. RADCLIFFE COOKE, C.W., *A Book about Cider and Perry*, 1898, pp.39-40; BARKER, B.T.P., *Cider Apple Production*, Ministry of Agriculture and Fisheries Bulletin 104, 1937, p.2; TUCKER, D.G., 'Millstone Making at Penallt, Monmouthshire', *Industrial Archaeology*, 1971, pp.233-4 and 321-33 which gives information on cider mills as well as on cider millstones; BRILL, E., *Life and Tradition in the Cotswolds*, 1973, pp.47-51; JENKINS, J.G., *Life and Tradition in Rural Wales*, 1976, p.160.

43. *New Scientist*, 20 December 1973, p.863 and 21 February 1974, p.520.

44. FUSSELL, G.E., *The Farmer's Tools*, 1952, pp.180-3; FUSSELL, G.E., 'Thrashing and Barn Machinery', *Journal of the Chartered Land Agents Society*, February 1960, pp.67-8. A box of this type was still in use on an Essex farm in the 1920s (WRIGHT, P., *Old Farm Implements*, 1961, p.51).

45. BOURNE, G., *Change in the Village*, 1912, 1966 ed., p.144; SCOTT WATSON, J.A., *History of the Royal Agricultural Society of England*, 1939, p.30; ROBERTS, R.O., *Farming in Caernarvonshire around 1800*, 1973, p.11; BLANDFORD, P., *Old Farm Tools and Implements*, 1976, p.159; JENKINS, J.G., *Life and Tradition in Rural Wales*, 1976, p.50.

46. For barn machinery see FUSSELL, G.E., *The Farmer's Tools*, 1952, pp.180-6; FUSSELL, G.E., 'Thrashing and Barn Machinery', *Journal of the*

Chartered Land Agents Society, February 1960, pp.61–71; JENKINS, J.G., *Life and Tradition in Rural Wales*, 1976, pp.49–50.

47. *Money, Milk and Milestones*, Hendon and District Archaeological Society, 1976, p.14.

48. For the milker's equipment see FUSSELL, G.E., *The English Dairy Farmer, 1500–1900*, 1966, pp.160, 162–3, 166; HARTLEY, M. and INGILBY, J., *Life and Tradition in the Yorkshire Dales*, 1968, pp.12, 32; ROLLINSON, W., *Life and Tradition in the Lake District*, 1974, pp.45–6; SMEDLEY, N., *Life and Tradition in Suffolk and North-East Essex*, 1976, p.119; INGRAM, A., *Dairying Bygones*, 1977.

49. For the milking machine see HALL, H.S., 'The Mechanisation of Milk Production', *British Agricultural Bulletin*, June 1951, pp.75–9; FUSSELL, G.E., *The Farmer's Tools*, 1952, pp.194–8; FUSSELL, G.E., 'Dairy Machinery', *Journal of the Chartered Land Agents Society*, March 1960, pp.117–20; JANNSSON, T., *The Development of the Milking Machine; a Historical Review*, Alfa-Laval, Tumba, Sweden, 1973.

50. For dairy utensils and equipment see FUSSELL, G.E., *The Farmer's Tools*, 1952, pp.191–4; EVANS, G.E., *Ask the Fellows Who Cut the Hay*, 1956, p.68; CHEKE, V., *The Story of Cheesemaking in England*, 1959; FUSSELL, G.E., 'The Evolution of Dairy Machinery in England', *Agricultural History*, 1963, pp.217–24; FUSSELL, G.E., *The English Dairy Farmer, 1500–1900*, 1966, pp.142–259; HARTLEY, M. and INGILBY, J., *Life and Tradition in the Yorkshire Dales*, 1968, pp.12–16; STEER, F.W., *Farm and Cottage Inventories of Mid-Essex, 1635–1749*, 1969, p.36; BRILL, E., *Life and Tradition in the Cotswolds*, 1973, pp.39–47; ROLLINSON, W., *Life and Tradition in the Lake District*, 1974, pp.45–8; BLANDFORD, P., *Old Farm Tools and Machinery*, 1976, pp.171–2; *Handbook*, National Museum of Wales, Welsh Folk Museum, 1976, p.18; SMEDLEY, N., *Life and Tradition in Suffolk and North-East Essex*, 1976, pp.119–21; COOPER, M., *Discovering Farmhouse Cheese*, 1978; NIELSEN, V.C., 'Cheesemaking and Cheese Chambers in Gloucestershire', *Industrial Archaeology*, 1968, pp.162–70, refers to cheese presses and other relics of 'this great industry' which were still to be found on many farms in the Vale.

61. For the shepherd's equipment see HUTCHINSON, T., *Machinery on the Farm*, 1949, p.36; FUSSELL, G.E., *The Farmer's Tools*, 1952, p.191; EVANS, G.E., *Ask the Fellows Who Cut the Hay*, 1956, pp.38–40, 50; WRIGHT, P., *Old Farm Implements*, 1961, pp.13, 20 for Littlebury Church; HARTLEY, M. and INGILBY, J., *Life and Tradition in the Dales*, 1968, pp.39, 42; GRANT, D. and HART, E., *Shepherd's Crooks*, 1972; BRILL, E., *Life and Tradition in the Cotswolds*, 1973, pp.118; PARTRIDGE, M., *Farm Tools through the Ages*, 1973, p.149; ROLLINSON, W., *Life and Tradition in the Lake District*, pp.79–80, 89–91; BLANDFORD, P., *Old Farm Tools and Machinery*, 1976, pp.156–7; JENKINS, J.G., *Life and Tradition in Rural Wales*, 1976, pp.51–4; INGRAM, A., *Shepherding Tools*

and Customs, 1977; *Stanmer*, Stanmer Preservation Society, n.d., p.26.

52. TROW SMITH, R., *A History of British Livestock Husbandry to 1700*, 1957, pp.47, 76–8, 120–3.

53. ROLLINSON, W., *Life and Tradition in the Lake District*, 1974, p.87.

54. For farm veterinary equipment see EVANS, G.E., *Ask the Fellows who Cut the Hay*, 1956, p.30; TROW SMITH, R., *A History of British Livestock Husbandry, 1700–1900*, 1959, pp.33–6, 186–8, 212–3, 316–9; EVANS, G.E., *The Horse in the Furrow*, 1960, pp.231–7; HARTLEY, M. and INGILBY, L., *Life and Tradition in the Yorkshire Dales*, 1968, pp.57–61; ROLLINSON, W., *Life and Tradition in the Lake District*, 1974, pp.74–81; SMEDLEY, N., *Life and Tradition in Suffolk and North-East Essex*, 1976, pp.108–11. For the early history of the veterinary profession see PUGH, L.E., *From Farriery to Veterinary Medicine 1785–1795*, 1962, which covers a longer period than the dates in its title suggest, from the founding of the first veterinary school in England in 1791 to the official recognition of the veterinary profession by Royal Charter in 1844. The Veterinary History Society, 32 Belgrave Square, London SW1, is concerned with all aspects of the history of animal disease, including early veterinary instruments and methods of treatment.

55. ROLLINSON, W., *Life and Tradition in the Lake District*, 1974, pp.78–9. For the Needfire and its survival in Scotland into the 19th century see DAVIDSON, T.D., 'The Untilled Field' *Agricultural History Review*, 1955, p.24.

56. HALLS, S.A., 'The Great Cattle Plague', Bulletin of the Ministry of Agriculture, Fisheries and Food, June 1965, p.43; *Animal Health. A Centenary 1865–1965*, HMSO, 1965, plate 2. Memorials to cattle buried during the cattle plague can be seen at Rectory Farm, Mucklestone, Market Drayton and Willoughbridge Lodge Farm, Pipe Gate, Market Drayton. The writer wishes to thank Mr F.T. Brown of the Ministry Veterinary Investigation Centre, Wolverhampton, for help with information on the location of these memorials and Mr and Mrs Bourne of the former farm and Mr John Turner of the latter for their permission to refer to their farms.

57. FLOUD, F., *The Ministry of Agriculture and Fisheries*, 1927, pp.11, 60–2; ERIKSON, A.B., 'The Cattle Plague in England, 1865–1867', *Agricultural History*, 1961, pp.94–103; *Animal Health. A Centenary, 1865–1965*, HMSO, 1965, pp.16–28, plate 2.

58. BRILL, E., *Life and Tradition in the Cotswolds*, 1973, p.76.

59. HARRIS, H., *Industrial Archaeology of Dartmoor*, 1968, p.156; HAYNES, R.G., 'Vermin Traps and Rabbit Warrens on Dartmoor', *Post-mediaeval Archaeology*, 1970, pp.147–64; ROLLINSON, R., *Life and Tradition in the Lake District*, 1974, pp.116, 149–50; ROLLINSON, R., *Lakeland Walls*, 1975, p.10; INGRAM, A., *Trapping and Poaching*, 1978.

60. For ropes, creels and sledges see JENKINS, J.G., *Agricultural Transport in Wales*, 1962, pp.11–19; HARTLEY, M. and INGILBY, J., *Life and*

Tradition in the Yorkshire Dales, 1968, pp.32, 34, 35; LONG, W.H., *Survey of the Agriculture of Yorkshire*, 1969, p.54; BRILL, E., *Life and Tradition in the Cotswolds*, 1973, p.79; ROLLINSON, W., *Life and Tradition in the Lake District*, 1976, p.93, 96; JENKINS, J.G., *Life and Tradition in Rural Wales*, 1976, pp.55–8; ATKINSON, F., *Life and Tradition in Northumberland and Durham*, 1977, p.43; Sledges were still being made and used in parts of Cumbria in the 1970s (*Guide to the Museum of Lakeland Life and Industry*, n.d. but after 1973, p.38).

61. JENKINS, J.G., *The English Farm Waggon*, 1972, pp.85–7.

62. GAUT, R.C., *A History of Worcestershire Agriculture*, 1939, p.450; *Farm Implement and Machinery Review*, 1 September 1950, p.740.

63. For carts and waggons see JENKINS, J.G., *Agricultural Transport in Wales*, 1962; ARNOLD, J., *The Farm Waggons of England and Wales*, 1969; JENKINS, J.G., *The English Farm Waggon*, 1972; BRILL, E., *Life and Tradition in the Cotswolds*, 1973, pp.53–8, who refers on p.58 to a waggon which continued in use into the 1950s; ROLLINSON, W., *Life and Tradition in the Lake District*, 1974, pp.94–6; VINCE, J., *Discovering Farm Carts and Waggons*, 1974; PORTER, S., 'From farm cart to waggon', *Countryman*, Winter 1974–5, pp.92–6; JENKINS, J.G., *Life and Tradition in Rural Wales*, 1976, pp.58–66; SMEDLEY, N., *Life and Tradition in Suffolk and North-East Essex*, 1976, pp.114–15; ARNOLD, J., *Farm Carts and Waggons*, 1977; JENKINS, J.G., *The English Farm Waggon*, 1972, pp.235–41 and VINCE, J., *Discovering Carts and Waggons*, 1974, pp.48–51, list places where carts and waggons can be seen. JENKINS, J.G., *Agricultural Transport in Wales*, 1962, pp.83–107 lists carts and waggons in the Welsh Folk Museum. See also VINCE, J., *Modelling Farm Carts* and *Modelling Farm Waggons*, both 1977.

64. For the Welsh survival see SCOURFIELD, E., *The Agricultural Gallery at the Welsh Folk Museum*, The National Museum of Wales, Welsh Folk Museum, 1976, p.4. See also *Farm Implement and Machinery Review*, 1 June 1950, p.240; JESSE, R.H.G., *A Survey of the Agriculture of Sussex*, 1960, p.83; EVANS, G.E., *Where Beards Wag All*, 1970, p.65; FOSTER, A., 'Working with Oxen', *The Countryman*, Spring 1973, p.138.

65. SEEBOHM, M.E., *The Evolution of the English Farm*, 1952, p.328 for Sussex; BRILL, E., *Life and Tradition in the Cotswolds*, 1973, p.102. One farmer in the Walsingham area of Norfolk continued to plough with oxen into the 1930s (personal communication, Miss Penny Davies, 1978).

66. For the working ox and its relics see EVANS, G.E., *Ask the Fellows who Cut the Hay*, 1956, p.82; MOORE, J.H., 'The Ox in the Middle Ages', *Agricultural History*, 1961, pp.90–3; JENKINS, J.G., *Agricultural Transport in Wales*, 1962, pp.50–1; FOSTER, A., 'Working with Oxen', *Countryman*, Spring 1973, pp.132–40; BRILL, E., *Life and Tradition in the Cotswolds*, 1973, pp.100–2; JENKINS, J.G., *Life and Tradition in Rural Wales*, 1976, p.36. For ox shoes see JENKINS, J.G., *Agricultural Transport in Wales*,

1962, p.51; SPARKES, I.G., *Old Horseshoes*, 1976, pp.12, 28–9. For the contemporary revived use of oxen on Cotswold Park Farm, near Cheltenham, and on Roe End Farm, near St Albans, see *Observer Magazine*, 25 September 1977, p.12.

67. For the horse and its relics see EVANS, G.E., *The Horse in the Furrow*, 1960; JENKINS, J.G., *Agricultural Transport in Wales*, pp.55–9; WRIGHT, P.A., *Salute the Carthorse*, 1971; KEEGAN, T., *The Heavy Horse, its Harness and Decoration*, 1974; WEATHERLEY, L., *Heavy Horse Handbook*, Southern Counties Heavy Horse Association, 1974; HART, E., *Heavy Horses*, 1976; VILLIERS, G., *The British Heavy Horse*, 1976; WHITLOCK, R., *Gentle Giants*, 1976. Articles on the farm horse are included in the journals *Heavy Horse and Driving*, Watmoughs, Idle, Bradford and *The Heavy Horse Magazine*, Claremont Publications, Horsham. For horseshoes, see SPARKES, I.G., *Old Horseshoes*, 1976, which includes a list of museums with relevant collections. For horsebrasses see BRILL, *Life and Tradition in the Cotswolds*, 1973, p.103; VINCE, J., *Discovering Horsebrasses*, 1974. The address of the National Horse Brass Society is 20 Greenhill Road, Sandford, near Bristol. Information on horseploughing matches can be obtained from the Southern Counties Heavy Horse Association, Rowley Drive, Cranleigh, Surrey or the Western Heavy Horse Society, Cranford House, Denver Road, Topsham, Devon.

68. JENKINS, J.G., *Life and Tradition in Rural Wales*, 1976, pp.51, 131, 155.

69. BRANCH-JOHNSON, W., *The Carrington Diary*, 1956, p.21; *Farmers Weekly*, 3 June 1966, p.49 for turbine; PETERS, J.E.C., *The Development of Farm Buildings in Western Lowland Staffordshire up to 1880*, 1969, pp.102–3; GRAY, J., 'An Industrialised Farm Estate in Berkshire', *Industrial Archaeology*, 1971, p.183 for turbine; ATKINSON, F., *Industrial Archaeology in the North-East*, 1974, vol.1, p.186; JENKINS, J.G., *Life and Tradition in Rural Wales*, 1976, pp.50–1; WARREN, D., 'Waterpower on Farms in West Somerset', *Somerset Industrial Archaeological Society Journal*, No.I, (1978), pp.5–12. See also the watermill publications of the Wind and Watermill Section of the Society for the Protection of Ancient Buildings.

70. DAVIES, W., *General View of the Agriculture of North Wales, 1810*, pp.121–2. No reference to the earlier use of steampower on the farm has been traced.

71. *Journal of the Royal Agricultural Society of England, 1879*, p.752; DICKINSON, H.W. and TITLEY, A., *Richard Trevithick*, 1934, pp.130–1, which shows the original type of boiler on p.130.

72. YOUNG, A., *General View of the Agriculture of Norfolk*, 1804, p.73.

73. WILLIAMS, M., *Steampower in Agriculture*, 1977, includes a section on stationary engines. A 10 hp engine erected on a Northumberland farm about 1835 to drive a thrashing machine, a grinder and also possibly a chaffcutter, which continued in use until shortly after the First World War, was reconditioned in 1967 by the Mechanical Engineering Department of Newcastle University and is now in the private Westside Museum of Mr J.E.

Moffitt, at Stocksfield, Northumberland. The author is grateful to Mr Moffitt for a loan of the unpublished thesis, *The New Bingfield Project*, prepared in 1967 by the students responsible for the reconditioning. An 1852 steam-engine is preserved at the North of England Open Air Museum, Beamish, Durham.

74. FUSSELL, G.E., *The Farmer's Tools*, 1952, p.74.

75. MIDDLETON, J.H., *Food Production in War*, 1923, pp.225-6, 240; *Farmers Weekly*, 24 December 1948, p.35; BONNETT, H., *Saga of the Steam Plough*, 1965, pp.173, 187.

76. BONNETT, H., *Saga of the Steam Plough*, 1965, pp.190, 198; BONNETT, H., *Discovering Traction Engines*, 1975, pp.24, 31. In 1975 'several' farmers were still using steam tackle (p.24), though presumably not commercially.

77. For steampower in the field see FUSSELL, G.E., *The Farmer's Tools*, 1952, pp.73-91; FUSSELL, G.E., 'Mechanically Hauled Ploughs', *Journal of the Chartered Land Agents Society*, August 1959, pp.290-9; SPENCE, C.C., *God Speed the Plough. The Coming of Steam Cultivation to Great Britain*, University of Illinois Press, 1960; BONNETT, H., *The Saga of the Steam Plough*, 1965; TRIST, P.J.O., *A Survey of the Agriculture of Suffolk*, 1971, p.195; VINCE, J., *Vintage Farm Machines*, 1973, pp.15-19; BONNETT, H., *Farming with Steam*, 1974; BONNETT, H., *Discovering Traction Engines*, 1975, pp.19-41; WILLIAMS, *Steampower in Agriculture*, 1977. In 1975 there were 169 steam ploughs in Britain, nearly all of them Fowler products (BONNETT, H., *Discovering Traction Engines*, 1975, pp.24, 41). The Steam Plough Club, 143 Norfolk Avenue, Sandersted, Surrey, is a national organization and issues a periodical newsletter. The National Traction Engine Club, 127 Greenstead Road, Loughton, Essex, issues the journal *Steaming*. There are a number of local societies concerned with the preservation of agricultural and other steam engines.

78. BRITTON, D.K. and KEITH, D.F., 'A Note on the Statistics of Farm Power Supplies in Great Britain', *The Farm Economist*, 1950, p.166. See also HARVEY, N., *A History of Farm Buildings in England and Wales*, 1970, pp.194-6.

79. See *A Pictorial Review of Barn Engines*, Vinteng Publications, Horsham, 1977. A monthly journal, *The Stationary Engine*, is published by Mr D.W. Edgington, Lodge Wood Farm, Hawkeridge, Westbury, Wiltshire. *Vaporising*, the journal of the National Vintage Tractor Club, 5 Minett Avenue, Rushwick, Worcester, includes material on barn engines.

80. WRIGHT, S.J., 'Expectations and reality', *Farm Mechanisation*, January 1954, p.5.

81. For the tractor see SCOTT WATSON, J., *History of the Royal Agricultural Society of England*, 1939, pp.99-103; WRIGHT, P.A., *Old Farm Tractors*, 1962; WILLIAMS, M., *Farm Tractors in Colour*, 1974; BLANDFORD, P., *Old Farm Tools and Machinery*, 1976, pp.30-42; CAWOOD, C.D., 'The

History and Development of the Farm Tractor', *Industrial Archaeology*, 1970, pp.264-92, 397-423; BALDWIN, N., *An Old Motor Kaleidoscope of Farm Tractors*, Old Motor Magazine, 1977; DEITH, C., *A Parade of Old Tractors*, Traction Engine Enterprises, 1978. The development of the tractor from 1915-23 is described in *Power Farming*, May 1976, pp.73-4; June, pp.73-4; July, pp.89-90 and August, pp.69-70. This journal from time to time contains descriptions of historical tractors and information for collectors on old tractors for sale. The National Vintage Tractor Club, 5 Minett Avenue, Rushwick, Worcestershire, issues a journal called *Vaporising*.

Chapter Nine

1. PETERS, J.E.C., 'Cogges Manor Farm, Witney', *Post-mediaeval Archaeology*, 1975, p.256; HILL, B. and KEMPSON, R.E., *Farm Buildings Capital in England and Wales*, Wye College, 1977, p.115. In terms of floor space, a little over a third of the farm buildings stock dates from before 1918. Most of this would date from the 18th or 19th centuries.

2. PETERS, J.E.C., *The Development of Farm Buildings in Western Lowland Staffordshire up to 1880*, 1969, reports the first substantial survey of farm buildings in their agricultural context and includes comprehensive general references; HARVEY, N., *History of Farm Buildings in England and Wales*, 1970, is a general source; HALL, R. de S., *A Bibliography of Vernacular Architecture*, 1972, contains sections on 'Treatises on the Design of Farmhouses and Buildings' and on 'Farmsteads and Individual Buildings'; WILIAM, E., 'Traditional Farm Buildings in Wales', *Amgueddfa*, Winter 1973, pp.2-14 (in Welsh) gives a general account of development; WILIAM, E., 'Farm Buildings in the Vale of Clwyd, 1550-1880' *Folklife*, 1973, pp.34-59, reports an area survey; BRUNSKILL, R.W., '*Illustrated Handbook of Vernacular Architecture*, 1974, includes a section on farm buildings; MESSENGER, P., 'Lowther farmstead plans; a preliminary survey', *Transactions of the Cumberland and Westmorland Antiquarian and Archaeological Society*, 1977, pp.327-51 report another area study. BRUNSKILL, R.W., 'Recording the Buildings of the Farmstead', *Transactions of the Ancient Monuments Society*, 1976, pp.115-50 illustrates the growing interest in this subject and *Traditional Farm Buildings*, published by the Arts Council in 1978, provides an introduction to it. For unpublished work see reference 60 in this chapter.

3. *Shielings and Bastles*, HMSO, 1970; ATKINSON, F., *Life and Tradition in Northumberland and Durham*, 1977, pp.55-7.

4. HARRIS, H., *The Industrial Archaeology of Dartmoor*, 1968, pp.146-9; HARVEY, N., *History of Farm Buildings in England and Wales*, 1970, pp.25, 27, 32-5, 47, 53-5, 62-3, 82, 102-3, 200, 210; NEWTON, R., *The*

Northumberland Landscape, 1972, p.137; WATSON, R., 'Some Fylde Longhouses', *Post-mediaeval Archaeology*, 1972, pp.198–202; MERCER, E., *English Vernacular Houses*, 1975, pp.34–50, including reference to Dorset longhouse on p.44 and laithe houses on p.55; SMITH, P., *Houses of the Welsh Countryside*, 1975, pp.144–5, 156, 280, 314; HURST, J., 'Villagers who kept moving house', *Observer Magazine*, 25 May 1975, p.22; JARRETT, M.G. and WRATHMELL, S., 'Sixteenth and seventeenth century farmsteads; West Whelpington, Northumberland', *Agricultural History Review*, 1977, pp.108–19.

5. HARVEY, N., *History of Farm Buildings in England and Wales*, 1970, pp.26, 33; WILIAM, E., 'Traditional Farm Buildings of Wales', *Amgueddfa*, Winter 1973, p.11.

6. HARRIS, H., *Industrial Archaeology of Dartmoor*, 1968, p.146; HARVEY, N., *History of Farm Buildings in England and Wales*, 1970, pp.32, 45; *Shielings and Bastles*, HMSO, 1970 pp.44–6; ROLLINSON, W., *Life and Tradition in the Lake District*, 1974, p.31; STEANE, J.M., *The Northamptonshire Landscape*, 1974, p.168; BRUNSKILL, R.W., *Illustrated Handbook of Vernacular Architecture*, 1974, p.153; BRUNSKILL, *Vernacular Architecture of the Lake Counties*, 1974, p.80; BERESFORD, G., 'The Mediaeval Manor of Penhallan in Cornwall', *Mediaeval Archaeology*, 1974, p.111; FINDLAY, W.M., *Oats*, 1956, pp.167–74, quotes mainly Scottish evidence but includes two English or Welsh references.

7. MARSHALL, W., *Rural Economy of the West of England*, 1796, vol. 2, pp.307–8.

8. For tithe barns see HARVEY, N., *History of Farm Buildings in England and Wales*, 1970, pp.41, 46.

9. PETERS, J.E.C., *The Development of Farm Buildings in Western Lowland Staffordshire up to 1880*, 1969, p.103; HELLEN, J.A., 'Agricultural innovation and detectable landscape margins – the case of wheelhouses in Northumberland', *Agricultural History Review*, 1972, pp.140–52; HARRISON, A. and J.K., 'The horsewheel in North Yorkshire', *Industrial Archaeology*, 1973, pp.247–64, 337–9, including reference to late example of wheelhouse on p.253; ATKINSON, F., *Industrial Archaeology of the North-East*, 1974, vol. I, p.188, 192 and entries in gazette in Vol. II; HUTTON, K., 'The distribution of wheelhouses in the British Isles', *Agricultural History Review*, 1976, pp.30–5; ATKINSON, F., *Life and Tradition in Northumberland and Durham*, 1977, pp.71–6; 'Horse gins in Somerset', *Somerset Industrial Archaeological Society Journal*, no. 1, (1978), pp.31–4. See also ROWLAND, J.H., 'Horsepower on the farm', *Country Life*, 29 January 1970, p.254,; *Country Life*, 12 March 1970, p.640, which refers to the wheelhouse in use in the 1930s; *Country Life*, 7 May 1970, p.1085; and WRIGHT, P.A., *Salute the Carthorse*, 1971, pp.46–7.

10. ATKINSON, F., *Industrial Archaeology of the North-East*, 1974, Vol. I,

pp.191–2, lists 32 surviving farm chimneys in Northumberland, Durham and Yorkshire.

11. PETERS, J.E.C., *The Development of Farm Buildings in Western Lowland Staffordshire up to 1880*, 1969, p.69; PETERS, J.E.C., Lecture on 'The Development of Barns' at Vernacular Architecture Group winter meeting 1977.

12. SCARFE, N., *The Suffolk Landscape*, 1972, p.172; BRANDON, P., *The Landscape of Sussex*, 1974, p.120; PARKER, R., *The Common Stream*, 1975, p.107 for Foxton.

13. JONES, E.L., 'The Bird Pests of British Agriculture in Recent Centuries', *Agricultural History Review*, 1972, p.115.

14. PETERS, J.E.C., *The Development of Farm Buildings in Western Lowland Staffordshire up to 1880*, 1969, pp.65–109; HARVEY, N., *History of Farm Buildings in England and Wales*, 1970, pp.23, 25, 36, 39–41, 43, 46, 56, 60, 77–9, 81, 94–6, 98, 112–4, 137, 138, 141, 173, 257, 262. See also cruck and framed construction in later section on Building Materials and Methods.

15. PETERS, J.E.C., *The Development of Farm Buildings in Western Lowland Staffordshire up to 1880*, 1969, pp.195–9; DOWLAND, C.J., 'Staddle Stones at Work', *Countryman*, Autumn 1976, pp.118–19; *Weald and Downland Open Air Museum Guide*, 1976, pp.18–21.

16. PETERS, J.E.C., *The Development of Farm Buildings in Western Lowland Staffordshire up to 1880*, 1969, pp.93–5; HARVEY, N., *History of Farm Buildings in England and Wales*, 1970, pp.89–90, 105–6, 142, 154, 199–200, 209; SMITH, P., *Houses of the Welsh Countryside*, 1975, pp.145–6, 152.

17. *Farmer and Stockbreeder*, 16 May 1961, p.86 for the 1885 silo at Lulham Court, Madley, Herefordshire; SMITH, E.J., 'Grandfather's Silage Boom', *Farmers Weekly*, 31 December 1965, pp.44–6; HARVEY, N., *History of Farm Buildings in England and Wales*, 1970, pp.184–7; ALLISON, K.J., *The East Riding of Yorkshire Landscape*, 1976, p.256.

18. PETERS, J.E.C., *The Development of Farm Buildings in Western Lowland Staffordshire up to 1880*, 1969, pp.190–1; HARVEY, N., *History of Farm Buildings in England and Wales*, 1970, pp.56, 113, 120, 142; SMEDLEY, N., *Life and Tradition in Suffolk and North-East Essex*, 1976, p.20; WILIAM, E., 'Farm buildings in North Wales', Lecture given at Vernacular Architecture Group winter meeting 1977.

19. TORR, C., *Small Talk at Wreyland*, 1927, p.27.

20. HARVEY, N., *History of Farm Buildings in England and Wales*, 1970, pp.131–2.

21. PETERS, J.E.C., *The Development of Farm Buildings in Western Lowland Staffordshire up to 1880*, 1969, pp.160–1; HARVEY, N., *History of Farm Buildings in England and Wales*, 1970, pp.130–1; WADE MARTINS, S., 'Factory farming in the 1850s', *Country Life*, 6 July 1978, pp.62–3 for Egmere Farm.

22. PETERS, J.E.C., *The Development of Farm Buildings in Western Lowland Staffordshire up to 1880*, 1969, pp.141-6, 150-8, 163-78; HARVEY, N., *History of Farm Buildings in England and Wales*, 1970, pp.49, 62, 69, 90, 133, 177-80.

23. HARVEY, N., *History of Farm Buildings in England and Wales*, 1970, pp.181-3, 229-31.

24. HARVEY, N., *History of Farm Buildings in England and Wales*, 1970, pp.59, 85-6, 133-4, 177, 203, 227, 252; ATKINS, P.J., 'London's intra-urban milk supply c. 1790-1914', *Transactions of the Institute of British Geographers*, 1977, pp.383-9; STOUT, A., 'Three Centuries of London Cow Keeping', *Farmers Weekly*, 18 August 1978, pp.v–xiii. For the last of the Liverpool cowkeepers see *Better Farming*, Spring 1975, p.6. This herd ceased production in the same year (Personal Communication, Miss V. Alexander, Milk Marketing Board).

25. NIELSEN, V.C., 'Cheesemaking and Cheese Chambers in Gloucestershire', *Industrial Archaeology*, 1968, pp.162-70; BRILL, E., *Life and Tradition in the Cotswolds*, 1973, pp.82-5.

26. PETERS, J.E.C., *The Development of Farm Buildings in Western Lowland Staffordshire up to 1880*, 1969, pp.178-9; HARVEY, N., *History of Farm Buildings in England and Wales*, 1970, pp.58, 78, 79, 101 (for 'Dairy' and 'Cheeseroom' inscriptions), 133, 178, 179, 203. See also reference 1 in this chapter and TORR, C., *Small Talk in Wreyland*, 1927, p.171 for 'Dairy' and 'Cheeseroom' inscriptions.

27. PETERS, J.E.C., *The Development of Farm Buildings in Western Lowland Staffordshire up to 1880*, 1969, pp.199-201; HARVEY, N., *History of Farm Buildings in England and Wales*, 1970, pp.24, 37, 39, 46, 55-6, 76, 100, 113-14, 136, 189-91, 206, 236-9.

28. PETERS, J.E.C., *The Development of Farm Buildings in Western Lowland Staffordshire up to 1880*, 1969, pp.201-4; ATKINSON, F., *Industrial Archaeology of the North-East*, 1974, Vol. II, p.247.

29. RAGLAN, LORD and FOX, SIR CYRIL, *Monmouthshire Houses*, pt. 2, 1953, p.81; WILIAM, E., 'Traditional Farm Buildings of Wales', *Amgueddfa*, Winter 1973, p.8; WILIAM, E., Lecture on 'The Farm Buildings of North Wales' at Vernacular Architecture Group winter meeting, 1977.

30. PETERS, J.E.C., *The Development of Farm Buildings in Western Lowland Staffordshire up to 1880*, 1969, pp.110-29; HARVEY, N., *History of Farm Buildings in England and Wales*, 1970, pp.46, 55-6, 81, 90, 106, 135.

31. JOBEY, G., 'A Note on Sow Kilns', *Journal of the University of Newcastle-upon-Tyne Agricultural Society*, 1966, p.38 for buchts; TROW SMITH, R., *History of British Livestock Husbandry, 1700-1900*, 1959, pp.8-9, for sheepfolds.

32. HARTLEY, M. and INGILBY, J., *Life and Tradition in the Dales*, 1968, p.38; TUCKER, D.G., 'A curious stone structure', *Industrial Archaeology*,

1970, pp.346–7; CAWOOD, C.L., *Industrial Archaeology*, 1973, p.441, and HARRIS, H., *The Industrial Archaeology of the Peak District*, 1971, pp.125, 146, 150–1 for sheep washes; NEWTON, R., *The Northumberland Landscape*, 1972, pp.33, 40 for stells.

33. HARVEY, N., *History of Farm Buildings in England and Wales*, 1970, pp.38–9, 56, 63, 136, 151, 202, 243, 255; BRUNSKILL, R.W., *Vernacular Architecture of the Lake Counties*, 1974, p.80.

34. PETERS, J.E.C., *The Development of Farm Buildings in Western Lowland Staffordshire up to 1880*, 1969, pp.204–6; 'The Dovecotes of Hertfordshire and the Saltpetre Industry', *Hertfordshire Countryside*, May 1970, pp.28–9; HARVEY, N., *History of Farm Buildings in England and Wales*, 1970, pp.41, 46, 57, 80–1, 102, 200, 210.

35. GARRAD, G.H., *Survey of Agriculture in Kent*, 1954, p.103; LOCKE, P.E., 'Landscape with oasts', *House of Whitbread*, Spring 1959, pp.17–21, which includes 1956 survey; HARVEY, N., *History of Farm Buildings in England and Wales*, 1970, pp.58, 97, 142, 196, 226–7; McRAE, S.G. and BURHAM, C.P., *The Rural Landscape of Kent*, 1973, p.193.

36. CHARLES, F.W.B., *Mediaeval Cruck Building and its Derivatives*, 1967, p.17 for Worcestershire survival; ALCOCK, N.W., *A Catalogue of Cruck Buildings*, 1973, includes farm buildings, mostly barns.

37. HEWETT, C.A., 'A Barn of Plantagenet Times', *Country Life*, 30 December 1971, p.1844 for Siddington barn; HEWETT, C.A., *Abbots Hall Barn*, Museum of East Anglian Life, 1975. See also RIGOLD, S.E., 'The Distribution of Aisled Timber Barns', *Vernacular Architecture*, 1971, p.20–4; CLARKE, D., Letter on previous article, *Vernacular Architecture*, 1973, p.20; CLARKE, D.W., 'Pennine Aisled Barns', *Vernacular Architecture*, 1973, pp.25, 26; BROWN, F.E., 'Aisled Timber Barns in Kent', *Vernacular Architecture*, 1976, pp.36–40; HEWETT, C.A., *The Development of Carpentry 1200 to 1700*, 1969 and HARRIS, R., *Discovering Timber-framed Buildings*, 1978.

38. BARLEY, M.W., in *The Agrarian History of England and Wales*, vol. 4, 1967, p.723; WILIAM, E., 'Traditional Farm Buildings in Wales', *Amgueddfa*, Winter 1973, p.13.

39. HUTTON, K., 'The Distribution of Wheelhouses in the British Isles', *Agricultural History Review*, 1976, p.35.

40. GRAY, J.R., 'An Industrial Farm Estate in Berkshire', *Industrial Archaeology*, 1971, pp.175–85; WADE MARTINS, S., *The Holkham Estate in The Nineteenth Century, with Special Reference to Farm Building and agricultural Improvement*, unpublished dissertation submitted to University of East Anglia for degree of Doctor of Philosophy, 1975, p.192 quoted by kind permission of the author.

41. HAGGARD, R., *A Farmer's year*, 1906, p.263 for 'clay lump'; GRIGSON, G., *An English Farmhouse*, 1948, p.42 for sarsen stone; WEBSTER, V.R.,

'Cruck framed buildings of Leicestershire', *Transactions of the Leicestershire Archaeological Society*, 1954, p.55. For building methods and materials generally see HARTLEY, M. and INGILBY, J., *Life and Tradition in the Yorkshire Dales*, 1968, pp.29, 107 for ling; PETERS, J.E.C., *The Development of Farm Buildings in Western Lowland Staffordshire up to 1880*, 1969, pp.2-5, 213-14, 217; HARVEY, N., *History of Farm Buildings in England and Wales*, 1970, pp.28, 42-3, 59, 61, 98-9, 109, 116, 143-4, 155, 197-9; SMITH, P., *Houses of the Welsh Countryside*, 1975, pp.146-7, 150-1, 324.

42. FOX, LADY EILEEN, 'A monastic homestead on Dean Moor, South Devon', *Mediaeval Archaeology*, 1958, pp.140-57.

43. MILLWARD, R., *Lancashire*, 1955, p.43 for Furness Abbey; *Country Life*, 25 June 1970, p.1262, for Toddington barn; HARVEY, N., *History of Farm Buildings in England and Wales*, 1970, pp.37, 64-5, 109, 171, 190; NEWTON, R., *The Northumberland Landscape*, 1972, p.138; BRILL, E., *Life and Tradition in the Cotswolds*, 1973, p.29, plates 49, 51; WILIAM, E., *Amgueddfa*, Winter 1973, p.13 for dating difficulty; HUTTON, K., 'The distribution of wheelhouses in the British Isles', *Agricultural History Review*, 1976, p.35 for Finchale Abbey; WADE MARTINS, S., lecture on 'Farm Buildings in East Anglia' at Vernacular Architecture Group winter meeting 1977 for Coke's Waterden Farm. The re-used crucks can be seen at Castle Farm Folk Museum, near Bath. For the Old Jordans barn see HARRIS, R., *The Finding of the Mayflower*, 1920; HORROCKS, J.W., 'The Mayflower', *Mariner's Mirror*, 1922, pp.8-9, 81-8, 140-7, 236-43, 354-62.

44. PETERS, J.E.C., *The Development of Farm Buildings in Western Lowland Staffordshire up to 1880*, 1969, pp.20-9.

45. See Chapter 3.

46. PETERS, J.E.C., *The Development of Farm Buildings in Western Lowland Staffordshire up to 1880*, 1969, pp.16-47; HARVEY, N., *History of Farm Buildings in England and Wales*, 1970, pp.22, 28, 31, 73-6.

47. HOSKINS, W.G., *Leicestershire*, 1957, p.32 for Theddingworth; HARRIS, A., *Rural Landscape of the East Riding of Yorkshire, 1700-1850*, 1961, p.11 for Holderness; PYE, N., *Leicester and Its Region*, 1972, p.254 for Wymesfold; HOSKINS, W.G., *English Landscapes*, 1973, p.84 for Great Gidding; STEANE, J.M., *The Northamptonshire Landscape*, 1974, p.239 for Pytchley; ALLISON, K.J., *The East Riding of Yorkshire Landscape*, 1976, p.160 for Wold Newton; PALLISER, D.M., *The Staffordshire Landscape*, 1976, pp.122-3 for Elford.

48. HOSKINS, W.G., *Leicestershire*, 1957, p.99; JONES, E.L., 'Eighteenth Century Changes in Hampshire Chalkland Farming', *Agricultural History Review*, 1960, p.15; POSTGATE, M.R., 'The Field System of Breckland', *Agricultural History Review*, 1962, p.87; HOSKINS, W.G., *Fieldwork in Local History*, 1967, p.75; WILLIAMS, M., 'The Enclosure and Reclamation

of the Mendip Hills, 1770–1870', *Agricultural History Review*, 1971, p.80; HOSKINS, W.G., *English Landscapes*, 1973, p.83.

49. HARTLEY, M. and INGILBY, J., *Life and Tradition in the Yorkshire Dales*, 1968, pp.1, 16; GRUNDY, J.E., 'Notes on the relationship between climate and livestock housing', *Vernacular Architecture*, 1970, pp.2–4 for Pennine barn; BRILL, E., *Life and Tradition in the Cotswolds*, 1973, p.17; PEARSALL, W.H. and PENNINGTON, W., *The Lake District*, 1973, p.251; ROLLINSON, R., *Life and Tradition in the Lake District*, 1974, p.31; BRUNSKILL, R.W., *Vernacular Architecture of the Lake Counties*, 1974, pp.81–6.

50. PETERS, J.E.C., *The Development of Farm Buildings in Western Lowland Staffordshire up to 1880*, 1969, pp.49–51; NEWTON, R., *The Northumberland Landscape*, 1972, p.139; BRUNSKILL, R.W., *Vernacular Architecture of the Lake Counties*, 1974, pp.80–1.

51. DICKSON, R.W., *General View of the Agriculture of Lancashire*, 1814, pp.96–7.

52. For case-studies of the historical development of particular farmsteads see BONHAM-CARTER, V., *Farming the Land*, 1959, pp.49–57; ALCOCK, N.W., 'A Devonshire Farm; Bury Barton, Lapford', *Transactions of the Devonshire Association*, 1966, pp.122–9; WADE MARTINS, S., 'Cannister Hall Farm', *Journal of the Norfolk Industrial Archaeology Society*, 1978, pp.22–4. See also the reference to Aldro Farm in Yorkshire in the later section on Two Estate Case-studies.

53. PETERS, J.E.C., *The Development of Farm Buildings in Western Lowland Staffordshire up to 1880*, 1969, pp.211–12; HARVEY, N., *History of Farm Buildings in England and Wales*, 1970, pp.126, 147–8, 171; EMERY, F., *The Oxfordshire Landscape*, 1974, p.186. See also later section on Two Estate Case-studies.

54. *Communications to the Board of Agriculture on Farm Buildings*, 1796, p.56.

55. STEANE, J.M., *The Northamptonshire Landscape*, 1974, p.167; HURST, J., 'Villagers who kept on moving house', *Observer Magazine*, 25 May 1975, p.22; WILIAM, E., 'Traditional Farm Buildings in Wales', *Amgueddfa*, Winter 1973, p.6.

56. The first recognisable description of this system in print appears in DANIEL GARRET'S *Designs and Estimates of Farmhouses etc. for the County of York, Northumberland, Cumberland, Westmorland and the Bishopric of Durham*, published in 1747. The first example of a farmstead built on this system found in an area survey in the Midlands dated from 1762 (PETERS, J.E.C., *The Development of Farm Buildings in Western Lowland Staffordshire up to 1880*, 1969, p.52). An interesting early example of this type of plan is found at Bachegraig, Tremeirchon, in Flintshire, which was built by Sir Richard Clough in 1567 (WILIAM, E., 'Farm buildings in the Vale of Clwyd, 1550–1880', *Folklife*, 1973, p.43).

57. PORTSMOUTH, LORD, 'The Fixed Equipment of the Farm', *Journal of the Royal Agricultural Society of England*, 1946, p.100.

58. DENTON, B., *Farm Homesteads of England*, 1863; PETERS, J.E.C., *The Development of Farm Buildings in Western Lowland Staffordshire up to 1880*, 1969, pp.48–65; HARVEY, N., *History of Farm Buildings in England and Wales*, 1970, pp.71–82, 111–17, 120–4, 159–63; JONES, J.L., 'Farming under a Victorian roof', *Country Life*, 12 October 1972, pp.919–20 for Eastwood Manor Farm; WILIAM, E., 'Farm Buildings in the Vale of Clwyd, 1550–1880', *Folklife*, 1973, p.38; *Shipley County Park, Derbyshire, Farm Interpretation Plan*, Countryside Commission, 1975, pp.10–11, 30–5; WOODHAMS, L., *The Story of an 1860 Agricultural Building*, Ministry of Agriculture, Fisheries and Food, Agricultural Development and Advisory Service, West Midlands Region, 1976; ROBINSON, J.M., 'Model Farm Buildings in the Age of Improvement', *Architectural History*, 1976, pp.17–32, describes the development of model farmsteads from 1730 to 1820, including a number of ornamental but non-agricultural accessories to the homes of the nobility and gentry, with a list of sites.

59. HARTLEY, M. and INGILBY, J., *Life and Tradition in the Yorkshire Dales*, 1968, p.29, 32; LONG, W.H., *Survey of the Agriculture of Yorkshire*, 1969, pp.54–5; PETERS, J.E.C., *The Development of Farm Buildings in Western Lowland Staffordshire up to 1880*, 1969, pp.31–5, 134–8; HARVEY, N., *History of Farm Buildings in England and Wales*, 1970, pp.82–3, 103, 146, 172; D'ARCY, J., 'Stone barns for better or worse', *Farmers Weekly*, 24 September 1971, p.111; HARRIS, H., *Industrial Archaeology of the Peak District*, 1971, p.146; BRUNSKILL, R.W., *Vernacular Architecture of the Lake Counties*, 1974, p.86; MERCER, E., *English Vernacular Houses*, 1975, p.49 for 17th century Dales buildings; SMITH, P., *Houses of the Welsh Countryside*, 1975, p.153; ALLISON, K., *The East Riding of Yorkshire Landscape*, 1976, p.164; WILIAM, E., lecture on 'The Farm Buildings of North Wales' at Vernacular Architecture Group winter meeting 1977.

60. POPHAM, J.H., *Farm Buildings, Function and Form*, Thesis for Diploma in Conservation Studies, Institute of Advanced Architectural Studies, University of York, 1973; WADE MARTINS, S., *The Holkham Estate in the Nineteenth Century, with Special Reference to Farm Building and Agricultural Improvement*, Dissertation submitted to University of East Anglia for degree of Doctor of Philosophy 1975. The writer is greatly indebted to both authors for their kind permission to use these unpublished theses. For farm buildings at Holkham see also ROBINSON, J.M., 'Estate Buildings at Holkham', *Country Life*, 21 November 1974, pp.1554–7 and 28 November 1974, pp.1642–5 and WADE MARTINS, S., 'Factory Farming in the 1850s', *Country Life*, 6 July 1978, pp.62–3.

Sources of Information

Museums

The national centres for agricultural history are the Museum of English Rural Life at Reading and the Welsh Folk Museum, National Museum of Wales, at St Fagans, near Cardiff. In addition, many local museums include agricultural departments and there are a number of farm museums and collections. Information on these is given in Shirley Toulson's *Discovering Farm Museums and Farm Parks*, 1977.

Journals

Industrial Archaeology and the *Industrial Archaeology Review* are national journals. Various local Industrial Archaeology Societies publish journals which sometimes contain agricultural material.

Mediaeval Archaeology and *Post-Mediaeval Archaeology* include reports on excavations of agricultural interest. Both list current work and the latter also lists recent publications.

Vernacular Architecture includes material on farm buildings.

The Agricultural History Review includes lists of current work and recent publications.

The Ark includes material on rare breeds of livestock.

The recently-formed Society for Landscape Studies intends to produce an annual journal called *Landscape History*.

Landscape Research includes material on historic landscapes.

Selective Book List

As is clear from the preceding chapters, the agricultural landscape of the country is very varied physically and historically. It is therefore best to seek local information from local libraries and museums.

One standard source of local information is the *Victoria County History* series of volumes, published by the University of London, Institute of Historical Research. These give documentary information, including sections on local agricultural history.

Another standard source is the series of county inventories published by the Royal Commission on Historical Monuments for England and the Royal Commission on Ancient and Historical Monuments for Wales. These list and describe physical survivals, including cultivation remains, warrens, farm buildings and other items of agricultural interest, with summaries of the various types of survival which they present by parish with details of location.

The following list gives only books of general interest

Farmland, Field Systems, Hedges, Walls, Water Supplies and Drainage
BAKER, A.R.H. and BUTLIN, R.A., *Studies of Field Systems in the British Isles*, Cambridge University Press, 1973
BAKER, A. and HARLEY, J.B., *Man Made the Land*, David & Charles, 1973
BERESFORD, M.W. and ST JOSEPH, J.K.S., *Mediaeval England, an Aerial Survey*, Cambridge University Press, 1958
BRITISH TRUST FOR CONSERVATION VOLUNTEERS, *Hedging*, 1975; *Dry Stone Walling*, 1977
CHAMBERS, J.D., *Laxton. The Last English Open Field Village*, HMSO, 1964
DARBY, H.C., *The Draining of the Fens*, Cambridge University Press, 1956
FIELD, J., *English Field Names. A Dictionary*, David & Charles, 1972
HARVEY, N., *Ditches, Dykes and Deep Drainage*, National Federation of Young Farmers Clubs, 1956; *Fields, Hedges and Ditches*, Shire Publications, 1976

HIGGS, J., *The Land*, Studio Vista, 1964

HOSKINS, W.G., *The Making of the English Landscape*, Hodder, 1955; *History from the Farm*, Faber, 1970; *English Landscapes*, BBC Publications, 1973

JEWELL, A., *Victorian Farming*, Shurlock, 1975

ORWIN, C.S., *The Open Fields*, Oxford University Press, 1967; with SELLICK, R.J., *The Reclamation of Exmoor*, David & Charles, 1970

POLLARD, E., HOOPER, M.D. and MOORE, N.W., *Hedges*, Collins, 1974

PUGSLEY, A.J., *Dewponds, Fact and Fable*, Country Life, 1939

RACKHAM, O., *Trees and Woodland in the British Landscape*, Dent, 1976

RAINSFORD-HANNAY, J., *Dry Stone Walling*, Stewartry of Kirkcudbright Dyking Committee, 1972

RAISTRICK, A., *The Pennine Walls*, Dalesman Books, 1976

REYNOLDS, P., *Farming in the Iron Age*, Cambridge University Press, 1976

ROLLINSON, W., *Lakeland Walls*, Dalesman Books, 1975

ROYAL COMMISSION ON HISTORICAL MONUMENTS, *Shielings and Bastles*, HMSO, 1970

TAYLOR, C., *Fields in the English Landscape*, Dent, 1975

Livestock

AINDOW, C.T. and BOWMAN, J.C., *Genetic Conservation and the Less Common Breeds of British Cattle, Sheep and Pigs*, Reading University, 1973

ALDERSON, L., *The Observer's Book of Farm Animals*, Warne, 1976; *The Chance to Survive*, David & Charles, 1978

TROW SMITH, R., *A History of British Livestock Husbandry to 1700*, Routledge & Kegan Paul, 1957; *A History of British Livestock Husbandry 1700–1900*, Routledge & Kegan Paul, 1959

Tools, Implements and Machines

ARNOLD, J., *The Farm Waggons of England and Wales*, David & Charles, 1969

BALDWIN, N., *An Old Motor Kaleidoscope of Farm Tractors*, Old Motor Magazine, 1977

BLANDFORD, P., *Old Farm Tools and Machinery*, David & Charles, 1976

BONNETT, H., *Saga of the Steam Plough*, David & Charles, 1965

BONNETT, N., *Farming with Steam*, Shire Publications, 1974; *Discovering Traction Engines*, Shire Publications, 1975

COLLINS, E.J.T., *Sickle to Combine*, Museum of English Rural Life, University of Reading, 1969

DEITH, C., *A Parade of Old Tractors*, Traction Engine Enterprises Ltd, 1978

FUSSELL, G.E., *The Farmer's Tools*, Andrew Melrose, 1952

INGRAM, A., *Dairying Bygones*, Shire Publications, 1977; *Shepherding Tools and Customs*, Shire Publications, 1977

JENKINS, J.G., *The English Farm Waggon*, David & Charles, 1972

PARTRIDGE, M., *Early Agricultural Machinery*, Evelyn, 1969; *Farm Tools Through the Ages*, Osprey, 1973

PASSMORE, J.B., *The English Plough*, Oxford University Press, 1930

SMITH, D.J., *Discovering Horse-drawn Farm Machinery*, Shire Publications, 1979

VINCE, J., *Vintage Farm Machines*, Shire Publications, 1973; *Old Farm Tools*, Shire Publications, 1974; *Discovering Carts and Waggons*, Shire Publications, 1974

WEATHERLEY, L., *Heavy Horse Handbook*, The Southern Counties Heavy Horse Association, 1972

WILLIAMS, M., *Farm Tractors in Colour*, Blandford, 1974; *Steampower in Agriculture*, Blandford, 1977

WRIGHT, P.A., *Old Farm Implements*, Black, 1961; *Old Farm Tractors*, David & Charles, 1962; *Salute the Carthorse*, Ian Allan, 1971

Farm Buildings

ARTS COUNCIL, *Traditional Farm Buildings*, 1978

BRUNSKILL, R.W., *Illustrated Handbook of Vernacular Architecture*, 1974

HARVEY, N., *A History of Farm Buildings in England and Wales*, David & Charles, 1970; *Old Farm Buildings*, Shire Publications, 1975

PETERS, J.E.C., *The Development of Farm Buildings in Western Lowland Staffordshire up to 1880*, Manchester University Press, 1969

Index

The numerals in *italics* refer to the illustration numbers